Stratigraphy
and
Geologic Time

Stratigraphy and Geologic Time

BROWN·FOUNDATIONS OF EARTH SCIENCE SERIES

John W. Harbaugh
Stanford University

WM. C. BROWN COMPANY PUBLISHERS
Dubuque, Iowa

Printed in U. S. A.

Biology

FOSSILS, PALEONTOLOGY
AND EVOLUTION

David L. Clark
University of Wisconsin

History

HISTORICAL GEOLOGY OF
NORTH AMERICA

R. L. Langenheim, Jr.
University of Illinois

STRATIGRAPHY AND
GEOLOGIC TIME

John W. Harbaugh
Stanford University

Oceanography **Geography**
Geodesy **Climatology**
Cartography

GEOGRAPHY,
CLIMATOLOGY
AND OCEANOGRAPHY

George R. Rumney
University of Connecticut

**Quaternary Studies and
Archeology**

PLEISTOCENE GLACIATION
AND THE COMING OF MAN

W. N. Melhorn
Purdue University

**Physical Geography and
Hydrology**

LANDFORMS AND
LANDSCAPES

Sherwood D. Tuttle
University of Iowa

Chemistry

EARTH MATERIALS

Henry Wenden
Ohio State University

Engineering and Mining

APPLIED EARTH SCIENCE

Daniel S. Turner
Eastern Michigan University

Physics

STRUCTURES, TECTONICS
AND GEOPHYSICS

John S. Sumner
University of Arizona

Astronomy

ASTRONOMY AND THE
ORIGIN OF THE EARTH

Theodore G. Mehlin
Williams College

BROWN
FOUNDATIONS
OF
EARTH
SCIENCE
SERIES

Man is a creature of the earth. Second to knowledge of man himself is the necessity to understand the earth. The comprehensive study of the earth and its phenomena is termed earth science. The subject area intersects numerous college disciplines. To gain a thorough scientific understanding of the earth, one must study astronomy, meteorology, oceanography, geology and geophysics, plus aspects of geography and engineering. Additionally, comprehension of these topics requires a prior knowledge of such areas as mathematics, physics, chemistry and biology.

The knowledge explosion which has occurred during the twentieth century has made this approach impossible for the educated layman. Nevertheless, the need to understand our earth has become increasingly necessary.

The **FOUNDATIONS OF EARTH SCIENCE** Series, designed for use at the introductory level, incorporates into the scientific study of the earth an understanding of what components comprise the earth, their distribution, and an understanding of how and why they exist as they are, and how they affect civilized man.

Geologists are most frequently asked variations of the following two questions: "How old is the earth?" "How did you figure out how old it is?" **Stratigraphy and Geologic Time,** in answering these questions, discusses the methods of dating and correlating the rocks of the earth, and in doing so is able to provide us with knowledge of the natural events of the past.

Preface

The objectives of this book are to outline and illustrate some of the important concepts that bear on geologic time, both from a qualitative and a quantitative point of view. Most of the qualitative concepts are interwoven with stratigraphy, which is that branch of geology dealing with layered rocks. Quantitative measurement of geologic time, however, involves radioactive decay. Thus this book has a two-fold division: the first five chapters deal largely with concepts of stratigraphy that pertain to qualitative age relationships; the sixth chapter deals with radioactive decay and its application to quantitative measurement of geologic time.

This book is intended for persons who have a knowledge of geology at least equivalent to that provided by an introductory course in physical geology. The book may be useful as a supplementary text in historical geology, and should be useful as a review for more advanced students in geology.

The author is indebted to various individuals for assistance. The drawings were prepared by Jerry Goodson. The manuscript was typed by Mrs. Judie Goodson and Mrs. Carol deRosia. Parts of the manuscript were read by the late Joseph J. Graham, Norman J. Silberling, Ernest I. Rich, Daniel F. Merriam, Edwin D. Goebel and the late Adolph Knopf.

Contents

Geologic Time Scale

TOPICS

Stratigraphy defined

Relative dating

Quantitative scale of time

Scale of geologic time

Establishment of geologic periods

INTRODUCTION

Stratigraphy is that branch of geology that deals with the study of stratified or layered rocks. Stratigraphy occupies a central position in geology (Figure 1), linking with historical geology, paleontology, sedimentology, structural geology, marine geology, glacial geology, and with economic geology, particularly petroleum geology and hydrogeology. Linkages with geomorphology, biology, paleoecology, chemistry, mineralogy, vulcanology and geophysics, although important, are less direct. None of these branches are sharply distinguished from each other. All intergrade more or less continuously and are components of a single broad spectrum, embracing all sciences.

Most stratified rocks are sedimentary rocks. Thus stratigraphy deals largely with sedimentary rocks, but it also deals with layered metamorphic rocks and volcanic rocks, as well as with layers of sediment that have not been consolidated into rock.

Stratigraphy is closely linked with geologic time. The role of time in geology is defined partly in terms of stratigraphic features. While time can be measured in years or hours, it can also be represented in a material sense by features of the earth whose age relationships may be determined through application of stratigraphic principles.

Stratigraphy, as other branches of geology, is pervaded with the concept of *uniformitarianism*, which implies that features of the earth

formed in the past have been produced by the same geological processes that are at work today. These processes are governed by un-
changing chemical and physical laws. While the features of the earth
have undergone change, and the rates of geologic processes may have
changed, the nature of the processes has not changed.

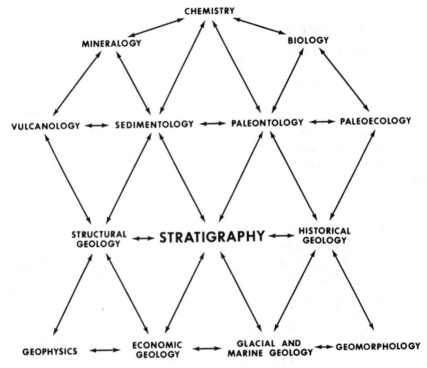

Figure 1. Relationship of stratigraphy to other branches of geology and
to chemistry and biology.

RELATIVE DATING

There are two principal kinds of dates in geology: relative dates
and absolute dates. Relative dates pertain to qualitative age relationships in which one geologic feature is either older, equal in age, or
younger than another feature. Absolute dates, however, pertain to estimates of actual ages in thousands or millions of years. The two kinds
of dates are compatible with each other. Geologists have dealt with
relative dates from the beginning of the science of geology, whereas
the techniques of absolute dating have been developed since about 1900.

Relative ages may be established through the application of a small number of principles of remarkable simplicity and universality:

(1) the law of superposition,
(2) the law of initial horizontality,
(3) faunal and floral succession,
(4) cross-cutting relationships, and
(5) relationships involving inclusions.

Superposition and Initial Horizontality

The law of superposition applies to any sequence of layered rocks (either sedimentary or extrusive volcanic) in which the layers have been formed one by one. It states that the oldest layer is on the bottom, and that higher layers are successively younger, the youngest being at the top (Figure 2). The law of superposition, in spite of its simplicity, is probably the most important generalization in geology. Its application has played a central role in the development of the geologic time scale and in helping discern evolutionary sequences of plants and animals.

In applying the law of superposition, at least two important assumptions are made. The first is that the sequence of layers was deposited more or less horizontally. While it is not essential that the layers have been perfectly horizontal, it is necessary to assume that they were not deposited vertically if their age relationships are to be known. This assumption is commonly described as the law of initial horizontality. The second assumption is that the layers have not been folded or faulted to such a degree that older layers rest above younger layers. Of course, there are actual examples where older layers now rest above younger. In these cases, successful application of the law of superposition requires that the folds and faults be considered.

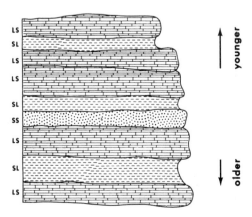

Figure 2. Sequence of strata illustrating law of super-position.

Development of the geologic time scale has involved application of the law of superposition. Knowledge of ancient geologic events is based largely on comparison of sequences of strata in different localities, the order of events at each locality being interpreted through the law of superposition and other laws.

Faunal and Floral Succession

Faunal and floral succession pertains to successive evolutionary changes in fossil organisms within a stratigraphic sequence. The order and direction of changes can be determined because higher layers are successively younger. Faunal and floral succession, coupled with super-position, provides a powerful tool in establishing the order of events when stratigraphic sequences in different localities are correlated with each other.

Cross-cutting Relationships

Cross-cutting relationships provide simple and effective means of establishing relative ages. In a cross-cutting relationship, the feature that is cut is older than the feature that cuts across it. Cross-cutting relationships are common, and include unconformities, faults and igneous intrusives. Their scales are highly variable, ranging from faults with displacements of tens of miles down to fractures with displacements of a few hundredths of an inch. It is not uncommon for faults and intrusives of different ages to intersect each other in complex fashion. The sequence of events at a locality can be worked out by successively interpreting a sequence of cross-cutting relationships. An example of two intersecting faults is represented in Figure 3, and a more complex

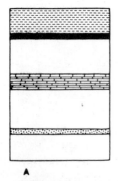 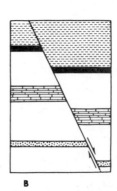 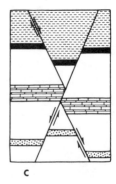

A   B   C

Figure 3. Progressive development of two intersecting faults: (A) before faulting; (B) after one fault has formed; (C) after second fault has formed.

set of cross-cutting relationships in Figure 4. The events leading to development of the geologic features represented in Figure 4A may be interpreted in a series of cross sections (Figure 4B to 4D) that are restorations of the geology prevailing at particular times in the past. The interpretations are based on application of superposition, initial horizontality and cross-cutting relationships.

Inclusions

Rock particles that form inclusions provide evidence of relative ages. The general rule is that particles are older than rock masses in which they are included. Two hypothetical examples are shown in Figure 5.

ROCKS AND GEOLOGIC TIME

Geologic time deals with interrelationships between rocks and time. Time can be defined in thousands or millions of years but geologic time has meaning only in relation to geologic features or events. In the geologic time scale (Table 1), the divisions of geologic time are defined and represented by the time required for the deposition of certain sequences of strata. For example, the Silurian Period is defined as the time during which the strata forming the Silurian System of England and Wales were deposited. Upon first consideration, this method of defining divisions of geologic time may seem strange and arbitrary. Yet, the use of stratigraphic sequences to define time is reasonable if one considers that virtually any sequence of strata has time significance, the relative ages of its layers being defined by the law of superposition.

In dealing with geologic time, we deal with three distinct types of units: (1) rocks alone, (2) time alone and (3) rocks and time in their relationship with each other. These units are described below and a summary is provided in Table 2.

Rock Units

Rocks may be arbitrarily classified according to their lithology — sandstone, mica schist, granite, etc. In addition, rocks may be segregated into a *geologic formation,* which is defined as an assemblage of rocks distinguished from other rock units for mapping purposes. This definition of a geologic formation is very general, applying to igneous, sedimentary, or metamorphic rocks. In practice, most formations have a degree of homogeneity, and rocks comprising a formation are generally of similar origin. Because formations are established for geologic mapping purposes, rather than having been defined to conform with specific criteria, precise definition of a geologic formation is difficult or impossible.

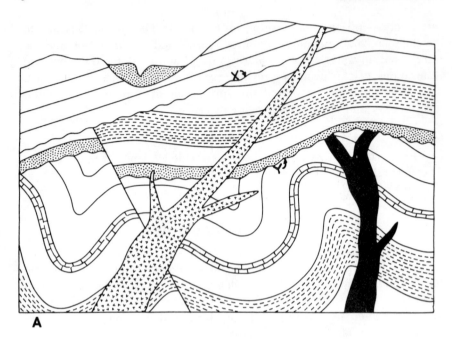

A

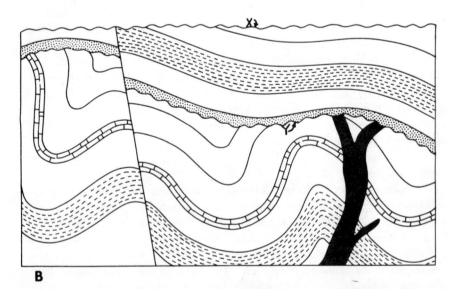

B

Figure 4. Cross sections that illustrate progressive "unraveling" of past events: (A) Present landscape and geologic structure. (B) Structure when unconformity X was formed; note that igneous intrusive shown with stippled pattern did not exist when unconformity X was formed. Unconformity is assumed to have been horizontal when formed.

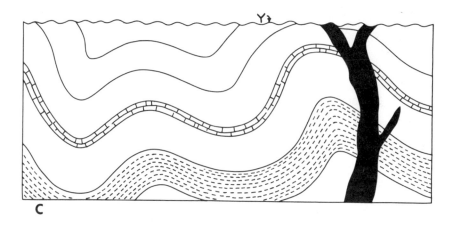

C

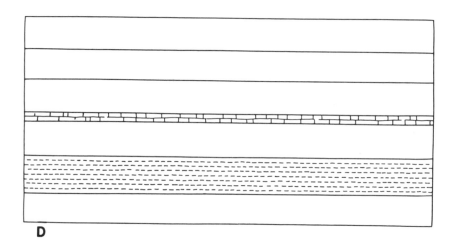

D

Figure 4. continued
(C) Structure when unconformity Y was formed. (D) Structure when
beds older than unconformity Y were deposited.

Formations bear geographic names that are commonly combined
with a lithologic term, as for example, the Leadville Limestone, Pikes
Peak Granite and Idaho Springs Schist. The term formation is often
used instead of a specific lithologic term, as in Franciscan Formation.
Formations may be divided into members which are persistent laterally.
Local subdivisions of small lateral extent form lentils or tongues. Two
or more adjacent formations which have important features in common

may be aggregated into a group, as, for example, the Arbuckle Group which consists of six formations.

Time-rock Units

Time-rock units are of hybrid nature in that they involve both rocks and time. Time-rock units generally involve sedimentary rocks, although lithologic characteristics are not essential to their definition. A time-rock unit represents geologic time in terms of the time required

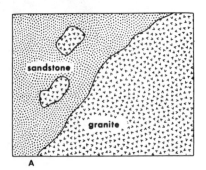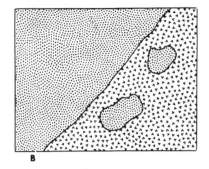

Figure 5. Age relationships based on inclusions: (A) Cobbles of granite within sandstone indicate that granite is older than sandstone (sandstone was deposited adjacent to granite). (B) Fragments of sandstone in granite indicate that granite is younger and is intrusive into sandstone.

for deposition of the time-rock unit. Correspondence between time-rock units and time units is shown in Table 2.

The smallest time-rock unit in general use is the *stage* which consists of strata which generally contain distinctive assemblages of fossils and which may be recognized and correlated in widely separated places. A stage is assumed to represent that particular span of geologic time during which the strata representing the stage were deposited. Substages, representing divisions of stages may also be recognized. Two or more stages may be combined to form a *series*. The most important time-rock units are the geologic *systems*, which consist of aggregations of lesser time-rock units. The systems are applied on a more or less world-wide basis and they form the framework of the geologic time scale. Each system is characterized by an assemblage of fossils that permits it to be generally distinguished from other systems. The boundaries between adjacent systems, however, are gradational and arbitrary in some places, resulting in sharing of fossil types and accompanying difficulty in exact definition of boundaries between systems.

TABLE 1

Geologic time scale in general use. Names of epochs in Cenozoic Era are
included; other epoch names are omitted. Estimates of time in millions of
years are modified from Holmes (1965), Kulp (1961), and others. There
is a margin of error in all estimates listed here, none being "absolute" in
the sense that they are known with a high degree of accuracy. Age estimates
are subject to change as age-dating techniques are improved and are
applied more and more widely.

Era	Period	Epoch	Millions of Years Ago	Duration in Millions of Years
Cenozoic	Quaternary	Recent Pleistocene	0-1	1
	Tertiary	Pliocene	1-13	12
		Miocene	13-25	12
		Oligocene	25-36	11
		Eocene	36-58	22
		Paleocene	58-63	5
Mesozoic	Cretaceous		63-135	72
	Jurassic		135-181	46
	Triassic		181-230	49
Paleozoic	Permian		230-280	50
	Pennsylvanian*		280-310	30
	Mississippian*		310-345	35
	Devonian		345-405	60
	Silurian		405-425	20
	Ordovician		425-500	75
	Cambrian		500-600	100

Precambrian No worldwide divisions of the Precambrian have been devised,
although various local classifications exist. By definition,
the Precambrian embraces the time between the origin of the
earth, and the beginning of the Cambrian Period.

Numerous radiometric dates are available for rocks that
were formerly deeply buried. Some of the groupings of age
dates that have been obtained from Precambrian rocks in different parts of North America are tabulated below:

(A) 925 to 1200 million years
1300 to 1450 million years
1620 to 1900 million years
2050 to 2100 million years
2425 million years
2500 to 2720 million years
3200 million years

(B) Certain meteorites have yielded age dates in the range
4500 to 4800 million years, suggesting a maximum age
of the earth and other planets of about 5000 million years.

*In Europe, the term Carboniferous is used, which is more or less equivalent to
the combined Pennsylvanian and Mississippian Periods.

TABLE 2

Classification of rock units, time-rock units, and geologic time units. Arrows indicate correspondence between units.

Rock Units	Time-rock Units	Time Units
		Era
	System ⟵——————⟶	Period
	Series ⟵——————⟶	Epoch
Group	Stage ⟵——————⟶	Age
Formation		
Member		

Time Units

Geologic time units are defined in terms of the time required for deposition of corresponding time-rock units. Time units are distinct from rock units, but they are meaningful in terms of corresponding time-rock units. The time unit corresponding to a stage is an *age*, a geological *epoch* corresponds to a series, and a geologic *period* corresponds to a *system* (Table 2). A geological *era* consists of an aggregation of periods.

SCALE OF TIME

A generally accepted classification of the geologic time scale is presented in Table 1. Some geologists and the geological surveys of some states and countries, however, employ time scales that differ slightly in details. The divisions of geologic time in use today stem largely from the nineteenth century, where they were proposed on the basis of studies of stratified rocks in the British Isles, Germany, Russia, France and the United States. When the individual systems were proposed, they were regarded as suitable stratigraphic divisions on the basis of stratigraphic and structural relationships. These divisions then began to serve as divisions of geologic time, eventually being incorporated into the time scale in use today. Although the time scale is arbitrary and subjective, it has proven to be of great utilitarian value and no doubt will continue to be used in the future.

Until the early part of the twentieth century, the geologic time scale dealt entirely with relative ages because, prior to that time, no effective means had been established for relating the divisions of geologic time to absolute numbers of years. The numerical age values for the geologic periods in Table 1 are estimates in current use that are based on radiometric age dating methods and are subject to revision. It should be borne in mind, however, that the divisions of geologic time in this scale are arbitrary. A time scale probably could have been established quite differently and still serve with equal usefulness. The availability of absolute age dates confirms that divisions of geologic time based on fossiliferous stratified rocks represent only a small part of total geologic time. Time that has elapsed since the start of the Cambrian Period represents only about 1/8 of the time that has elapsed since the earth was created (current estimates place the age of the earth between 4 and 5 billion years). The remaining 7/8 of geologic time, lumped into the Precambrian, is represented by rocks that are now only partly accessible to us at the surface of the earth. Consequently, divisions of geologic time based on stratigraphic and paleontological methods represent only a small fraction of total geologic time.

The periods have been grouped into three eras: (1) the Paleozoic Era (era of "ancient life"), (2) the Mesozoic Era (era of "middle life") and (3) the Cenozoic Era (era of "recent life"). The Tertiary and Quaternary Periods are commonly divided into epochs. The older periods may be similarly divided, although the names of their epochs are less commonly used.

The geologic time scale (Table 1) was not conceived as a coherent whole, but instead evolved piecemeal during the last century, emerging in part as a result of extended personal conflict between influential early geologists. The origins of the individual geologic systems are outlined below.

Cambrian

The Cambrian Period is that span of time in which the Cambrian System was deposited. Cambrian rocks take their name from *Cambria*, the Latin name for Wales. Outcrops of rocks in Wales (Figures 6 and 7) furnish the "type" for all Cambrian rocks, with which rocks elsewhere in Europe and on other continents are correlated and compared. Even though Cambrian rocks in other regions may be different from those in Wales, the overall boundaries of the Cambrian System are defined by reference to the type Cambrian in Wales. Thus, rocks in Wales have been defined as Cambrian, whereas rocks of comparable age elsewhere are established as Cambrian by comparison with those in Wales.

The establishment of the Cambrian System has an interesting human history. Adam Sedgwick, a clergyman and professor at Cambridge University, applied the name "Cambrian" in the 1830's to a series of dark sandstones or graywackes in North Wales known as the Old Graywacke. Sedgwick began near the bottom of the sequence of beds comprising

Figure 6. Simplified geologic map of British Isles showing generalized distribution of Cambrian, Ordovician and Silurian rocks.

the Old Graywacke, and worked toward the top, placing all of the beds in his Cambrian System. More or less at the same time, another distinguished geologist, Sir Roderick Murchison, began his studies of the same sequence of beds, but beginning at the top instead of the bottom. Murchison classified the Old Graywacke as part of his Silurian System, a name likewise taken from an ancient Welsh tribe. Some of the strata which both Sedgwick and Murchison had defined overlapped. The result, beginning in the early 1840's, was a prolonged interval of disagreement between the two geologists, for neither was willing to give ground in the definition of the two systems.

Ordovician

The Ordovician System was proposed in 1879 by the English geologist Charles Lapworth to resolve the dilemma of the overlap between Sedgwick's Cambrian System and Murchison's Silurian System. The upper part of Sedgwick's Cambrian and the lower part of Murchison's Silurian were combined and set aside in a new system named the Ordovician, the name Ordovician being derived from an early Celtic

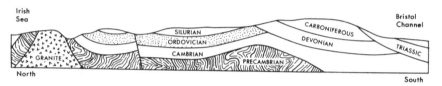

Figure 7. Simplified north-south geologic cross section through Wales showing generalized configuration of Cambrian, Ordovician, Silurian and younger rocks. Adapted from A. K. Lobeck, **Geological Map of Europe** (Columbia University Press, 1942).

tribe, the Ordovices, that resided in Wales. The bottom and the top of the Ordovician System, as thus defined, are fairly easily separated from adjacent rocks by the presence of angular unconformities (Figure 8) which denote breaks in the sedimentary sequence as a result of folding, uplift and erosion. The Ordovician rocks in Wales, like the

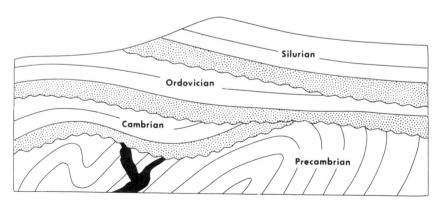

Figure 8. Schematic geologic cross section emphasizing unconformities separating Cambrian, Ordovician and Silurian Systems in Wales. Unconformities are denoted by wavy lines.

Cambrian, furnish a type standard against which Ordovician rocks in other parts of the world may be compared and subsequently defined.

Silurian

The Silurian System was proposed in 1835 by Murchison to include strata exposed in Wales and adjacent western England. The name is adapted from that of the Silures, an early tribe that inhabited the region. As stated previously, the lower part of Murchison's Silurian System was subsequently reclassified to form part of the Ordovician System.

Devonian

The Devonian System was named by Sedgwick and Murchison in 1839, the name being taken from Devonshire in southwestern England (Figure 9). It was at this locality that fossiliferous marine strata, occurring stratigraphically between Silurian strata below and Carboniferous strata above, were first recognized. The Devonian strata in Devonshire, however, are so highly folded and faulted that they do not serve very well as a type. Instead, Devonian rocks in western Germany, northeastern France, and southern Belgium serve much better as a type to which other Devonian strata may be compared. In North America, marine Devonian strata are particularly well displayed in an east-west outcrop belt in northern New York State.

Mississippian

The name Mississippian is American in origin. In Europe, the name Mississippian is not generally applied, and instead, strata that are roughly equivalent in age are termed Lower Carboniferous. The Upper Carboniferous, in turn, is more or less equivalent to the Pennsylvanian of North America. The name Carboniferous (Figure 9) was first applied in 1822 to coal-bearing strata in England. In England, and in many other places, there is marked contrast between the Lower and Upper Carboniferous. Consequently, the segregation of the Carboniferous into the two distinct systems or subsystems is logical. Accordingly, the name Mississippian was proposed by Alexander Winchell, a prominent American geologist, in 1869 and applied to Lower Carboniferous strata exposed in the bluffs of the Mississippi River and elsewhere in the upper part of the Mississippi River drainage basin.

Pennsylvanian

The name Pennsylvanian was applied in 1891 by H. S. Williams, an American geologist, to Upper Carboniferous strata exposed in parts

Figure 9. Generalized distribution of outcropping Devonian strata and Carboniferous strata in the British Isles.

of Pennsylvania. Strata originally defined as Pennsylvanian include some deposits that were later regarded as Permian by some geologists. Currently there is unresolved debate as to the wisdom of segregating Permian strata from strata originally defined as Pennsylvanian.

Permian

The Permian system was named in 1841 by Murchison after rocks exposed in the province of Perm, which lies between Moscow and the

Ural Mountains in Russia (Figure 10). In North America, the standard Permian deposits are in southwestern Texas and southeastern New Mexico.

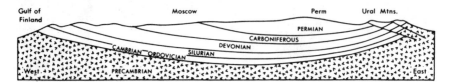

Figure 10. Generalized east-west geologic cross section from the Ural Mountains to the Gulf of Finland showing distribution of Permian and older strata. Adapted from Lobeck (Columbia University Press, 1942).

Triassic

The name Triassic was first given in 1834 by the German geologist von Alberti. The name refers to the threefold sequence in Germany (Figure 11), in which the lower and the upper divisions consist of red sandstones and shales deposited under nonmarine conditions, whereas the middle division consists of marine shales and limestones. The threefold division of the Triassic System observed in Germany is not generally present in strata of Triassic age in other parts of the world; consequently, the name Triassic may be regarded simply as a proper name and no longer implies a threefold division.

Jurassic

The Jurassic was the first system to be formally defined. The name Jurassic is adapted from the Jura Mountains in the Alps between France and Switzerland (Figure 12). The name was first applied by Von Humboldt in 1799 to strata exposed in the Jura Mountains, but the

Figure 11. Diagrammatic east-west geologic cross section extending from the Danube River to the Rhine River graben, showing threefold division of Triassic System. Adapted from Lobeck (Columbia University Press, 1942).

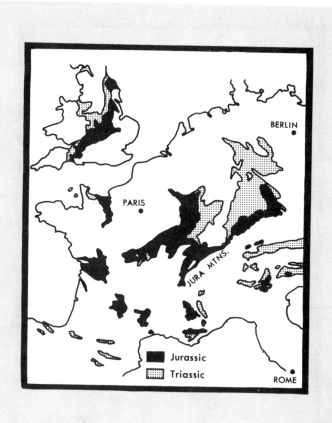

Figure 12. Distribution of outcropping Triassic and Jurassic strata in western Europe.

stratigraphic limits of the Jurassic System were later extended by incorporation of other strata.

Cretaceous

The name "Cretaceous" is adapted from the Latin *creta,* which means chalk. The name was applied in 1822 by d'Halloy, a Belgian, to chalky strata in England and France (Figure 13).

Tertiary

The name "Tertiary" is a holdover from an obsolete geologic time scale proposed in 1759 by the Italian Giovanni Arduino. His classi-

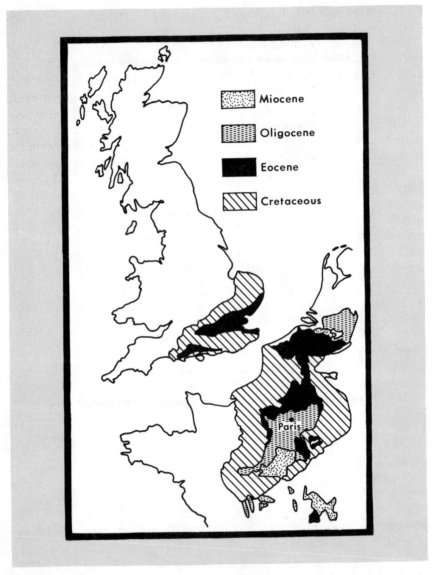

Figure 13. Generalized outcrops of Cretaceous, Eocene, Oligocene and Miocene strata in England and northern France.

fication had four major divisions: Primary, Secondary, Tertiary and Quaternary. The Primary division consisted of the oldest rocks, and the youngest sediments were included in the Quaternary, the Secondary and Tertiary being intermediate. Arduino's time scale has long since been superseded, but, the names Tertiary and Quaternary have been retained as proper names.

The epochs or divisions of the Tertiary and Quaternary are of particular interest and importance. From oldest to youngest, the Tertiary is divided into the Paleocene, Eocene, Oligocene, Miocene and Pliocene Epochs. Three of these divisions stem from a proposal made in 1833 by the English geologist Charles Lyell. He classified the epochs according to the proportion of species of mollusks present as fossils, relative to those that live today. Lyell's original classification included the Eocene, Miocene and Pliocene Epochs; the Oligocene was proposed by Beyrich in 1854 and the Paleocene by Schimper in 1874. If we include the Pleistocene Epoch of the Quaternary Period, the "Lyellian" scheme for division of the Cenozoic is shown in Table 3. While Lyell's method of subdividing the Tertiary and Quaternary has theoretical merit, it has not proven satisfactory in practice. Some Tertiary and Quaternary sediments are not very fossiliferous, prohibiting comparison on a percentage of living molluscan species basis. Then, too, the labor of making quantitative comparisons makes the theory difficult to apply. The names of the epochs, however, are firmly embedded in the geological literature and, as divisions of time, have proven useful.

Quaternary

The name Quaternary stems from Arduino's classification. The beginning of the Quaternary Period has been defined by some geologists as the start of the "ice age," when large continental glaciers appeared. Other definitions are based on stratigraphic sequences. The division of the Quaternary into the Pleistocene Epoch and the Recent Epoch is

TABLE 3

Epochs of the Cenozoic Era.

Epoch	Percentage of living Molluscan species (modification of Lyell's classification method)	Meaning of prefix adapted from Greek
Pleistocene	90–100	*pleist*—most
Pliocene	50– 90	*pleion*—more
Miocene	20– 40	*meion*—less
Oligocene	10– 15	*oligos*—little
Eocene	1– 5	*eos*—dawn
Paleocene	0	*palaius*—ancient

based on the assumption that the earth has emerged from the ice age, the close of which marks the end of the Pleistocene. There is evidence to suggest that the earth is still in an ice age, and that the present is an interval between major glaciations. Accordingly, the merit for sub-division of the Quaternary into two epochs is lessened. We should keep in mind, however, that all divisions of geologic time are arbitrary and it is doubtful that any purely objective method of classification could be developed. Thus, the division into Recent and Pleistocene Epochs is justified on a practical basis.

The Geologic Eras

The three eras, Cenozoic, Mesozoic and Paleozoic, are aggregations of geologic periods. Sedgwick introduced the name Paleozoic, signifying "ancient life," in 1838 for all the rocks in the Cambrian and Silurian Systems. Paleozoic has been subsequently used in a time sense and has been broadened to include the periods from Cambrian to Permian. The name Mesozoic ("middle life") and Cenozoic ("recent life") were introduced by Phillips in 1849. The Mesozoic embraces the Triassic, Jurassic and Cretaceous Periods. The Cenozoic embraces the Tertiary and Quaternary Periods.

ABSOLUTE SCALE OF TIME

The geologic time scale presented in Table 1 contains estimates, in millions of years, of the duration of each of the periods and of the Cenozoic epochs, and of their ages in terms of total elapsed time. These estimates have been obtained by making radiometric age determinations of rocks obtained at critical locations. The methods of radiometric age dating are taken up in Chapter 6, but general principles of their application are outlined below.

Radiometric age dates are based on the following assumptions: (1) that the specimen containing radioactive material that is analyzed is representative of the age of the geologic body being dated; (2) that the specimen analyzed has neither lost nor gained radioactive material nor its daughter products due to external causes, such as solution or precipitation, and (3) that the rate of decay of the radioactive parent material is known with sufficient accuracy.

Application of radiometric dating methods to a geologic body is not without difficulty. First, there are sources of error inherent in the analytical process; second, there exists the possibility of gains or losses in the specimen analyzed due to processes other than radioactive decay; third, there may be difficulty in establishing the stratigraphic position of the geologic body, particularly in the case of igneous bodies. For example, the "stratigraphic position" of an intrusive igneous body is generally determinable only through its relationship to sedimentary or layered extrusive volcanic rocks whose stratigraphic position is known. While such relationships are simple in principle, they may be complex and obscure in practice. Figure 14 shows, diagrammatically, how the minimum and maximum relative ages of an igneous intrusion can be determined. Ideally, the span between maximum and minimum ages should be small if the absolute date yielded by the intrusive body is to be useful in providing a date for the geologic time scale. Fortunately, the stratigraphic position of layered volcanic rocks that are interbedded in sedimentary sequences can be relatively accurately established. Many critical age dates in the absolute scale of time have been provided by layered volcanics.

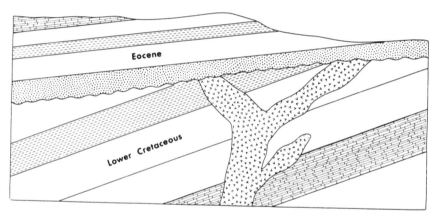

Figure 14. Diagrammatic geologic cross section illustrating determination of relative age of igneous intrusive. Based solely on evidence shown in diagram, maximum age of intrusive is slightly younger than uppermost bed in Lower Cretaceous and minimum age is slightly older than lower bed in Eocene.

REFERENCES

FENTON, C. L. and FENTON, M. A., *Giants of Geology.* Garden City: Doubleday and Co., 1952 (Fascinating account of development of geology as a science.)

HOLMES, ARTHUR, *Principles of Physical Geology.* New York: Ronald Press Co., 1965. (Chapter 13 deals with quantitative scale of geologic time.)

KULP, J. L., "Geologic Time Scale," *Science,* 133: 1105-1114, 1961. (Tabulates critical radiometric dates that apply to geologic time scale since start of Cambrian Period.)

LOBECK, A. K., *Geologic Map of Europe.* New York: The Geographical Press, Columbia University, 1942. (Map and cross sections provide simplified introduction to geology of Europe.)

MOORE, R. C., *Introduction to Historical Geology.* New York: McGraw-Hill Book Co., 1958. (Chapter 3 deals with development of geologic time scale.)

STOKES, W. L., *Essentials of Earth History,* 2nd ed., Englewood Cliffs: Prentice-Hall, Inc., 1966. (Chapters 3 and 4 are recommended.)

WELLER, J. M., *Stratigraphic Principles and Practice.* New York: Harper and Brothers, 1960. (Detailed exposition of stratigraphic principles.)

WOODFORD, A. O., *Historical Geology.* San Francisco: W. H. Freeman and Co., 1965. (Chapter 3 deals with development of geologic time scale.)

SUMMARY OUTLINE

Stratigraphy
Uniformitarianism
  Guiding principle in geology

Relative dating
  Superposition
  Initial horizontality
  Floral and faunal succession
  Cross-cutting relationships
  Inclusions

Divisions of geologic time
  Relationships between rocks and time
  Rock units
  Time-rock units
  Time units

Scale of geologic time
  Proportion of earth's age represented by time scale
  Establishment of the geologic periods
  Arbitrary nature of scale of time
  Aggregation of periods into eras
  Epochs of the Cenozoic Era

Quantitative scale of time
  Applying radiometric age dates to geologic features

Stratigraphic Correlation

INTRODUCTION

Geologic correlation is concerned with the mutual equivalence of rock units. Unfortunately, no simple definition of correlation is possible because of its diverse meanings. Rock units may be equivalent in (1) time, (2) lithology, or (3) fossil content. Particular rock units may be equivalent in all three of these aspects; others in only one or two. While the concept of correlation pertains to all types of rocks, we are concerned here with the correlation of sedimentary rocks.

Stratigraphic correlation plays a central role in geology. Without it there would be no geologic time scale, nor would interpretation of geologic history be feasible. One of the general objectives of historical geology is to establish the synchroneity of events. Establishing the equivalence of mountain-building crustal movements on different continents, for example, requires that the time relationships between the rocks involved be established. In turn, this is largely a matter of stratigraphic correlation.

The concepts of correlation are strongly influenced by the magnitude of features involved and their distance apart. Over short distances, an objective in correlation is to ascertain whether rocks exposed at different localities are parts of rock units that are, or were, physically continuous (Figure 15). Over long distances, however, an objective is to establish time equivalence. In making correlations between North

America and Europe, for example, there is little possibility that rock units were physically continuous (Figure 16). To complicate matters, however, strata of certain ages may have highly distinctive lithologies, such as chalk deposits of Cretaceous age. Thus, chalk deposits may be roughly correlated in different parts of the world on the basis of similar lithology, even though not necessarily part of a unit that was once physically continuous.

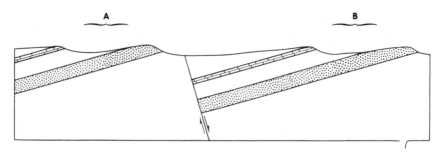

Figure 15. Geologic cross section showing correlation of beds that were formerly physically continuous. Outcrops at localities A and B are correlated on the basis of lithology and sequence.

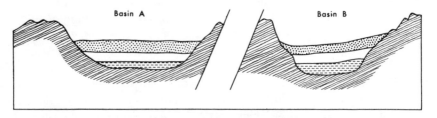

Figure 16. Diagram to show objective in correlating hypothetical beds deposited simultaneously in two basins that are not physically continuous. Basin A and basin B are separated by an appreciable distance.

To further cloud objectives, a rock formation may be physically continuous and lithologically and paleontologically homogenous, but may differ significantly in age from place to place. While establishment of time equivalence is an ideal, in practice, correlation more often consists of establishing lithologic or paleontologic equivalence, with the assumption that a degree of time equivalence is involved. Lithologic and paleontologic evidence can be viewed directly, whereas time relationships can only be inferred.

Evidence that is available commonly has critical bearing on correlations. We may distinguish two general classes of evidence, physical and paleontological.

PHYSICAL EVIDENCE FOR CORRELATION

Lateral Continuity

The simplest method of correlation is to follow strata as they crop out. If strata are well exposed, as in the Grand Canyon for example, it is possible to trace individual rock units for many miles. Lacking such good exposures, beds may be followed on aerial photographs. In some regions, particularly where the strata dip gently, outcrops of strata of varying erosional resistance influence topography to such extent that continuous units may be followed by observing topographic benches and steeper sloping scarps (Figure 17).

Lithologic Similarity

Lithologic similarity is important where exposures are intermittent and direct tracing is impossible. Unless lithologies involved are highly distinctive, however, correlations on the basis of lithology alone are likely to be insecure. Few sedimentary deposits are of similar lithology throughout, even if formed essentially simultaneously from place to

Figure 17. Alternating resistant and poorly resistant stratigraphic units may be correlated by observing their influence on topography.

place. Local lithologic variations, termed *facies,* may reflect local differences in sediment sources, or depositional environment. If the objective is to ascertain time equivalence, miscorrelations may result from strict adherence to lithologic similarity (Figure 18).

Sequence of Strata

The orderly sequence of different kinds of beds in a stratigraphic succession may, in itself, be extremely helpful in establishing correlations. Even if lithologies of beds are not particularly distinctive, their sequence may be highly distinctive. Figure 19 illustrates two hypothetical outcrops in which the sequence of lithologies provides part of the evidence on which the strata are correlated. Correlation by sequence is not without hazard, however. Some sedimentary deposits are composed of se-

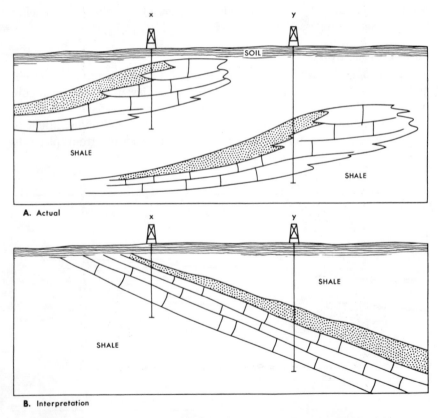

Figure 18. Hypothetical geologic cross sections showing effect of miscorrelation: (A) actual relationships of lensing limestone and sandstone bodies; (B) an erroneous correlation based on lithologic similarity.

quences of beds that are repeated over and over again, termed *cyclic sedimentation*, and may be miscorrelated if they cannot be traced laterally.

Electrical and Radioactivity Logs of Wells

Strata penetrated by oil wells may be correlated by means of their electrical and radioactive properties. These properties are measured by devices lowered into the wells, and are recorded in the form of curves

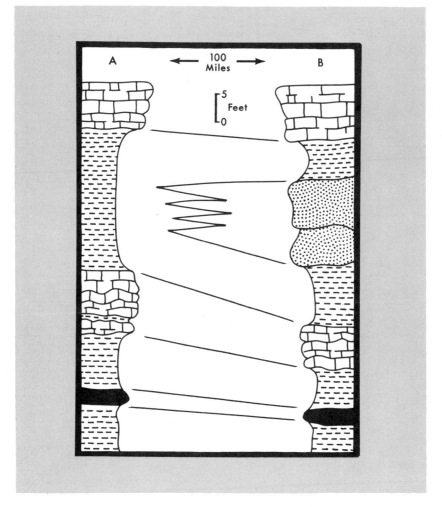

Figure 19. Correlation between two hypothetical outcrops. Sequence of beds, coupled with lithologic information, forms basis for correlations. Sandstone at B is presumed to grade laterally into shale between B and A.

which represent variations in electrical or radioactive properties of the rocks with depth (Figure 20).

In electric logging methods, two properties are measured: (1) the ability of rocks to conduct a current (or conversely, the electrical re-

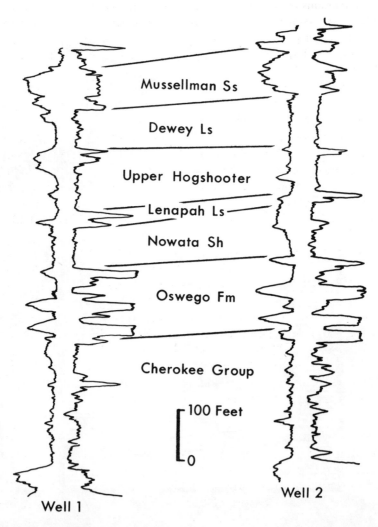

Figure 20. Correlation of strata of Pennsylvanian age encountered in two oil wells in north-central Oklahoma on basis of electrical logs. Curves have been redrawn from actual records made at wells. Right curve at each well is plot of resistivity versus depth; left curve is plot of self potential versus depth.

sistivity of rocks), and (2) the "self potential" of rocks. The ability of rocks to conduct a current is a function of the proportion of pore space in the rock and the type of fluids filling the pores, such as salt or fresh water. Rock minerals themselves are good insulators; thus, electrical conductivity or resistivity measurements directly reflect properties pertaining to fluids. Electrical self potential, likewise, is related to presence of fluids. The self potential stems from a battery effect caused by chemical reactions of fluids in the drilling mud introduced in drilling of wells, which comes in contact with rocks adjacent to the borehole and with fluids in pores of the rocks.

The electrical properties of rocks are physical aspects that are as useful in stratigraphic correlation as those properties that can be seen directly. The electrical properties can be measured even though the rocks do not crop out anywhere. In fact, most of our knowledge of buried strata is obtained through logging of oil wells.

Logging devices that measure variations in natural radioactivity in rocks (quite apart from radiometric dating methods) are also useful for stratigraphic correlation. Variations in radioactivity are due to differences in proportions of radioactive materials, as, for example, the proportions of radioactive potassium (potassium-40) in grains of orthoclase feldspar in sandstone, and metallo-organic compounds containing uranium that are present in some shales and sandstones.

Correlation with electrical logs or radioactivity logs is, to a large extent, a matter of matching curves. Individual stratigraphic units tend to have distinctive electrical or radioactivity "signatures" on the logs, and, in regions where the strata extend over large areas with only gradual lateral changes, correlation may be a relatively simple matter. In a sense, we may regard the use of electrical and radioactivity logs as an extension of correlation methods based on lithologic similarity and stratigraphic sequence. Other types of well logging methods are also useful for stratigraphic correlation, including sonic logs which record variations in the velocity of sound in rocks versus depth.

Key Beds

Some layers of sediment have been deposited essentially simultaneously over large areas. These may be termed "key beds" and they provide correlatable time horizons within stratigraphic sequences. The most reliable key beds consist of thin beds of volcanic ash extending over large areas. Fine ash blown from a single volcanic eruption may be transported by wind and deposited as a distinct layer that extends over hundreds or thousands of square miles. If preserved by burial, volcanic ash commonly undergoes chemical alteration to bentonitic clay. Other types of key beds consist of thin beds rich in fish-scales, or isolated beds rich in fossil oysters or corals that record the former presence of widespread populations on the sea floor that flourished during brief intervals of time.

Correlation by Radiometric Dating

In spite of the great success of radiometric dating in supplying a quantitative basis for the geologic time scale, radiometric dating has not been as widely used for stratigraphic correlation as one might think. The reason is that radiometric age dates are not sufficiently accurate for many correlations. For example, an average error of only one percent in rocks that are 500 million years old is equivalent to an error of five million years. For many correlation purposes, this would be a large error. Yet, an average error of one percent would represent an almost ideally low proportion of error in radiometric age dating. On the other hand, radiometric age dating provides the only valid method of correlation of Precambrian rocks over large areas.

PALEONTOLOGICAL EVIDENCE FOR CORRELATION

As correlation is attempted over greater and greater distances, physical evidence, except for radiometric age dating, becomes progressively less reliable and fossils become relatively more important. Of course, fossils are also useful for correlations over short distances. The use of fossils is based on progressive evolution through time. Thus, particular species of plants and animals may be good indexes of a certain interval of geologic time by virtue of having arisen by evolution early in the interval and having disappeared through extinction at the end of the interval. These progressive appearances and disappearances underlie the law of faunal and floral succession, which, of course, is a simple and powerful concept in geology.

William Smith was one of the first to note the relations between fossils and the arrangement of stratified rocks. He was a surveyor and engineer involved in the construction of canals and roads in England from 1787 to 1839. Smith observed that different layers of rock could be identified by the fossils that they contain. He was able to predict the depth of layers to be encountered in excavations by reference to fossils contained in other rocks exposed at the surface. The importance of Smith's discovery was not immediately apparent, and several decades elapsed before his methods were accepted and he became known as the "Father of Stratigraphy."

In Smith's day, living species or fossils, were believed to be the result of special creation. Different fossils in different beds could be explained by assuming that cataclysmic events exterminated all life periodically, and the repopulation took place when totally new species were created. The practical value of fossils having been established, there seemed little reason at first to question the cataclysmic or special creation theory. Later, however, it was observed that species that occur together in a particular bed did not occur together in underlying or overlying beds. In other words, it came to be realized that the stratigraphic ranges of species that occurred with each other were not everywhere the same. It was necessary to conclude that creation and extinction have taken place continually, rather than periodically, thus establishing the concept of faunal and floral succession. With acceptance of Darwin's theory of evolution, the basis of correlation by fossil species became more complicated. Since the theory of evolution implied that each species had gradually evolved from an ancestral species, and in turn, may have evolved further into one or more descendent species, it was realized that species may not have abrupt limits and that correlations based on fossils are necessarily influenced by the gradational aspect of fossil species.

Index Fossils

Fossil species differ in their usefulness as stratigraphic indexes. Ideally, an index fossil should be (1) easily identified and distinguished from all other fossils, (2) have lived during a relatively short span of geologic time, (3) be widely distributed geographically, (4) have lived in different sedimentary environments and occur in different types of sedimentary rocks, and (5) be abundant. Not many fossils meet all of these requirements. For example, some organisms preserved as fossils are both widely distributed geographically and lived only during a short span of geologic time, but they may have lived in such special environments that they are rare and are not generally useful. Other fossils that are of little use as stratigraphic indexes have persisted for long intervals of time with little or no change.

Since the usefulness of an index fossil is partly related to the span of time in which the organism lived, it is essential to determine the stratigraphic range of the fossil. Specimens collected in a single region may not be sufficient to determine the range of the organism. Collections in other regions may reveal that the fossil occurs in older or younger beds. In fact, the complete range of a particular fossil may never be accurately known because of the possibility that the youngest or oldest beds in which the fossil formerly occurred are no longer preserved.

Detailed correlations over long distances with fossils are strongly influenced by rate of migration or dispersal. If it is assumed that each species arose at a single time and place, the presence of a single species in two (or more) widely separated localities implies migration of the species. The accuracy of a time correlation depends partly on how fast species have migrated. Careful observation of the rates at which modern marine organisms have migrated suggest that the time involved for species to migrate, under favorable conditions, is not great in proportion to geologic time; nevertheless, the time required for migration is sufficiently long to have some effect on accuracy of time correlations over long distances.

Assemblages of Fossils

Assemblages of several fossil species are generally more useful for correlation than a single species. One reason is that a single species may not be present at all localities which are to be correlated, whereas an assemblage of fossils is more likely to be present. Of course, since some species may be present or be absent, an assemblage may vary from place to place. A second reason is that an assemblage may permit more detailed correlation because of different, but overlapping, stratigraphic ranges of individual species. Figure 21 illustrates three hypothetical

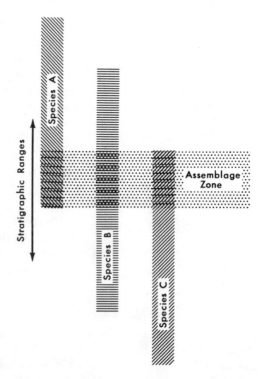

Figure 21. Diagram illustrating overlapping ranges of three hypothetical species which define a narrower assemblage zone.

species that have different stratigraphic ranges, but which overlap to form a narrower zone in which all three occur together as an assemblage. In this hypothetical example, species A evolved immediately before the basal bed in the stratigraphic unit containing the assemblage zone was deposited, species B appeared well before the basal bed was deposited and continued to live on long afterwards, whereas species C, though also arising well before the basal bed was deposited, became extinct just after the uppermost bed in the stratigraphic unit had been deposited. Thus, the interval of time through which species A, B, and C lived simultaneously is shorter than that of any of the individual species.

Correlations are also influenced by differences in the geographic ranges of fossil species. It is obvious that no organism is adapted to live in all places on earth; few plants or animals that live in the tropics also live at cold, high latitudes. Each organism has its environmental niche, although some organisms can exist through a much greater range of environmental conditions than others. Organisms most generally useful in correlation are those that lived in ancient seas because the bulk of fossiliferous sedimentary rocks accessible on the continents are shallow-water marine deposits.

References

DUNBAR, C. O. and RODGERS, J., *Principles of Stratigraphy.* New York: John Wiley and Sons, 1957. (Chapter 16 deals with correlation.)

MOORE, C. A., *Handbook of Subsurface Geology.* New York: Harper and Row, 1963. (Chapters 4 and 5 provide an excellent review of electrical and radioactivity well logging methods and Chapter 2 with their use in stratigraphic correlation.)

STOKES, W. L., *Essentials of Earth History,* 2nd ed. Englewood Cliffs: Prentice-Hall, Inc., 1966. (Chapter 6 deals with correlation.)

WOODFORD, A. O., *Historical Geology.* San Francisco: W. H. Freeman and Co., 1965. (Chapter 7 provides a good discussion of correlation through use of zones of fossils.)

SUMMARY OUTLINE

Objectives in correlation
    Equivalence in time
    Equivalence in lithology and fossil content

Evidence for correlation
    Lateral continuity
    Lithologic similarity
    Sequence of strata
    Well logs

Index fossils
    Role of evolution
    Ideal qualities of index fossils
    Assemblages of fossils

CHAPTER

3

Unconformities

INTRODUCTION

A stratigraphic unconformity is a relationship that represents a break in a sequence of beds. Because a sequence of beds has time significance, an unconformity also represents a gap in the record of geologic time. There are four general types of unconformities: (1) *nonconformities,* in which layered rocks rest upon unstratified igneous or poorly stratified highly metamorphosed rock (Figure 22A); (2) *angular unconformities* in which the strata below the unconformity are cut off and are overlain at an angle by the beds above the unconformity (Figure 22B); (3) *disconformities* in which the strata above and below an unconformity are parallel, but the unconformity itself is not parallel to bedding (Figure 22C); and (4) *paraconformities* in which a break in the sequence and the strata above and below the break are all parallel (Figure 22D). Of course, these four types intergrade and, viewed broadly, all may have a more or less common origin (Figure 23).

Unconformities can be correlated. Unlike stratified rocks, however, unconformities do not possess distinctive properties in themselves. Recognition and correlation of unconformities depends on understanding the relationship with rocks that lie above and below an unconformity. For example, a particular unconformity may be recognized because it occurs everywhere beneath a certain formation. The rocks immediately beneath an angular unconformity are different from place to place,

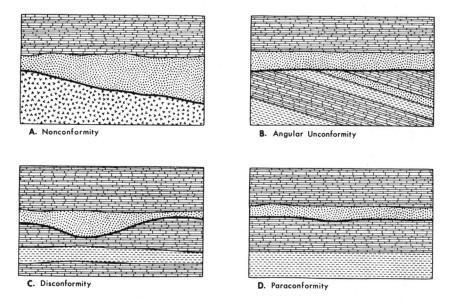

Figure 22. Geologic cross sections illustrating four types of unconformities. Heavy lines denote unconformities.

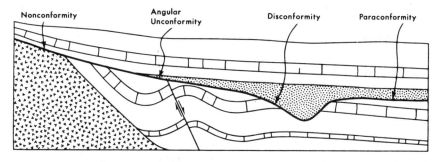

Figure 23. Geologic cross section showing four types of unconformities which form components of a single widespread unconformity.

contrasting with a paraconformity, along which the same rock units may persist for substantial distances.

Angular Relationships

The angular relationships of beds above and below an unconformity bear on its origin. If the beds below are inclined at an angle with respect to the unconformity, folding, uplift and erosion may be inferred to have occurred prior to deposition of strata above the unconformity. Overlying beds not parallel to an unconformity (Figure 24) may signify deposition in a rising sea which progressively transgressed over the land, forming deposits that overlapped higher and higher over the sloping former land surface.

Beds that are parallel to an unconformity (paraconformity) signify lack of folding before development of the unconformity and resumption of sedimentation without folding. Paraconformities may be difficult to

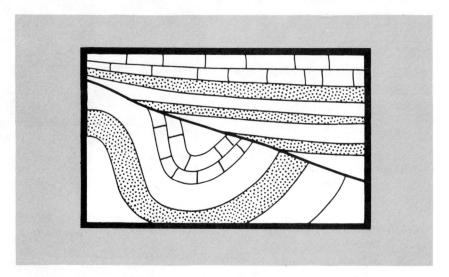

Figure 24. Geologic section showing beds formed by progressive overlap upon an unconformity.

recognize unless they can be laterally correlated with more readily recognized unconformities, or fossils present in beds both above and below provide evidence of a missing interval of time.

Magnitude of Unconformities

Unconformities vary widely in magnitude. One measure is geographic extent. Some unconformities may be traced over only a few square miles whereas others span a million square miles or more. Another measure is the degree of structural deformation that occurred after the rocks beneath the unconformity were formed and before the overlying beds were laid down. The disturbed rocks beneath unconformities may record events of mountain-building proportions, as evidenced by presence of faults beneath unconformities with thousands of feet of displacement and by folds of large magnitude. Interpretation of ancient mountain building is generally based partly on structural relationships at unconformities.

Some unconformities represent relatively large amounts of "missing" geologic time. For example, Merriam (1964) has estimated that at least half of the time that has elapsed since the start of the Cambrian Period is not represented by strata in Kansas, even though all of the systems, Cambrian through Quaternary, are represented in Kansas. The missing time is largely represented by unconformities in the sequence of strata in Kansas.

Unconformities as a Measure of Periodic Disturbance

Early geologists recognized that major unconformities, many of which marked disturbances or revolutions of mountain-building proportions, appeared to have formed at about the same times in widely different parts of the world. This led to the belief that major unconformities record series of disturbances that occurred periodically. For example, three intervals of structural deformation in western Europe resulted in the building of great mountain chains: (1) the Caledonian revolution separating the Silurian and Devonian Periods; (2) the Hercynian revolution during the Carboniferous and Permian Periods, and (3) the Alpine revolution which occupied much of the Tertiary Period. These three revolutions have counterparts in North America. Some of the folding of the Appalachian chain occurred at roughly the same time as the Hercynian revolution, and widespread mountain-building activity in the Rocky Mountain region partly accords in time with Alpine folding in Europe.

The similarity in time of occurrence of these revolutions has given support to the idea that major mountain-building disturbances have occurred on a worldwide basis with more or less regular periodicity. These ideas have been generally warmly received because they accord with early geological thought which placed much emphasis on catastrophism. Furthermore, the worldwide disturbances appeared to furnish a reasonable basis for division of geologic time into eras and periods. It was generally accepted that every geologic period had been set apart from preceding and succeeding periods by disturbances which served as "punctuation marks" in geologic history. Table 4 provides a list of major geological revolutions that seem to bound geologic periods.

Although the separation of geologic periods by major disturbances or revolutions is appealing, the method is not wholly satisfactory. Many disturbances have occurred in the middle of geologic periods rather than at their boundaries. In fact, disturbances of mountain-building pro-

TABLE 4

Names of major "revolutions" that have been considered to separate the geologic periods in parts of North America (and one from Europe). Position of "revolutions" are shown with wavy lines.

Periods	Names of "Revolutions"	Regions
Quaternary		
〜〜〜	Cascade	Pacific Northwest
Tertiary		
〜〜〜	Laramide	Rocky Mountains
Cretaceous		
〜〜〜	Nevadan	Sierra Nevada
Jurassic		
〜〜〜	Palisades	Northeastern U.S.
Triassic		
〜〜〜	Appalachian	Appalachian Mountains
Permian		
〜〜〜	Marathon	Central southwestern U.S.
Pennsylvanian		
〜〜〜	Ouachita	Arkansas, Texas, Oklahoma
Mississippian		
〜〜〜	Acadian	New England
Devonian		
〜〜〜	Caledonian	Europe
Silurian		
〜〜〜	Taconic	New England
Ordovician		
〜〜〜	Vermontian	New England
Cambrian		
〜〜〜	Killarney	Ontario, Canada
Late Precambrian		

portions have probably occurred continuously through geologic time if large areas, such as the whole of North America, are considered. Furthermore, there is evidence that most revolutions have not been abrupt, but instead, have taken place over extended intervals of time. Establishing the boundaries between systems is further complicated by the lack of unconformities at boundaries of systems in some regions, where unbroken sequences of strata indicate essentially continuous deposition.

The wisdom of designating disturbances or revolutions to mark the boundaries between geologic systems is still hotly debated. There is increasing scepticism as to the validity of worldwide "revolutions", and many geologists do not regard them as valid criteria for establishing divisions of geologic time. Nevertheless, there is little doubt that disturbances have varied in frequency and magnitude over the earth and that certain major disturbances have occurred more or less simultaneously on different continents.

REFERENCES

DUNBAR, C. O., and RODGERS, J., *Principles of Stratigraphy*. New York: John Wiley and Sons, 1957. (Discusses many aspects of stratigraphy, including unconformities.)

MERRIAM, D. F., "Geologic History of Kansas," *Kansas Geological Survey Bulletin*: 162, 1964. (Pages 161 to 177 provides good description of unconformities in Kansas.)

WELLER, J. M., *Stratigraphic Principles and Practice*. New York: Harper and Bros., 1960. (Chapter 11 deals with unconformities.)

SUMMARY OUTLINE

Types of unconformities
Nonconformities, angular unconformities, disconformities and paraconformities

Magnitude of unconformities
Significance of unconformities in representing "missing" geologic time

Unconformities as evidence of ancient crustal disturbances
Periodic versus continuous disturbance

4

Thickness Maps and Paleogeologic Maps

TOPICS

Thickness maps
Paleostructural interpretation
Sources of error

Alternative interpretations
Paleogeologic maps
Structural history

THICKNESS MAPS

Interpretation and dating of ancient structural disturbances depend partly upon critical analysis of variations in thickness of stratified rocks and on relationships at unconformities. The tools that are needed include thickness maps and sections for analyzing thickness variations, and paleogeologic maps and sections for studying unconformities.

A thickness map employs contour lines to portray thickness variations of a sedimentary unit. The individual contour lines denote intervals of equal thickness, and are analogous to lines of equal elevation on a topographic map. Thickness maps are also termed *isopachous* maps (*iso* meaning equal and *pachous* representing thickness). A thickness map differs from a topographic map, however, in that it does not represent a real surface, but instead, portrays numerical data which represent thickness variations. Information for construction of thickness maps (and for vertical sections that show thickness variations) may be obtained from a variety of sources, including geologic maps, measurements at outcrops, and from logs of wells that penetrate buried strata.

Thickness maps and sections enable interpretations to be made of the amount of warping or folding that took place during the time represented by a given stratigraphic interval. The use of thickness maps for this purpose is based on the assumption that the strata were essentially horizontal when deposited (law of initial horizontality). There are important exceptions to this generalization, however. For example, beds deposited on relatively steeply sloping submerged surfaces are not initially horizontal. On the other hand, stratified rocks of marine origin that extend over large areas in the interiors of the continents probably were deposited more or less horizontally. The assumption of original horizontality provides a simple means of restoring the former structure of a stratigraphic unit. If its upper surface is plotted horizontally, the lower surface of the unit assumes the structure that it had at the time that the upper surface was deposited (Figure 25). In plotting the upper

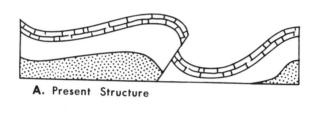

A. Present Structure

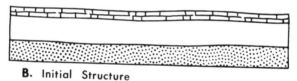

B. Initial Structure

Figure 25. (A) Present structure restored to (B) time of deposition by plotting beds horizontally.

surface horizontally, folds and faults that affect the unit may be ignored if they formed after the upper surface was deposited. On the other hand, all beds that lie beneath the horizontal datum bed will assume the structural attitude that they had when the datum bed was being deposited. Such a geologic section may be termed a *paleostructural section* because it portrays ancient structure. Of course, beds that now lie above the datum bed must be omitted because they had not been deposited when the datum horizon was formed (Figure 26).

Paleostructural sections have some interesting properties. Consider a paleostructural section (Figure 26B) in which the thickness interval between the datum bed and some lower marker bed varies from place to place. The thicker intervals may be interpreted as places where downwarping occurred, whereas the thinner intervals denote places where relative upwarping occurred.

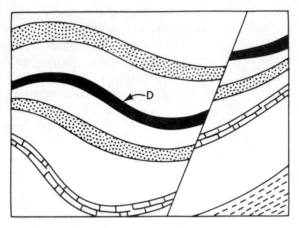

A. Present Structure

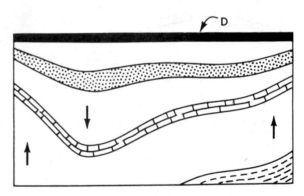

B. Structure at time of deposition of bed D

Figure 26. Present structure (A) provides information for restoration of structure (B) at time of deposition of bed D. Vertical arrows indicate warping inferred from thickness variations.

Interpretations similar to that shown in Figure 26 are justified in dealing with broad, gentle folds or warps whose geographic dimensions are measured in miles. When sediments are deposited over broad areas, the depositional processes tend to even out irregularities. Topographically low places, and places where relative downwarping occurs, tend to receive more sediment than high places. The result is a tendency for a more or less horizontal depositional surface to form, providing the general basis for validity of the law of initial horizontality.

The law of initial horizontality also can be applied (with caution) to unconformities. Unconformities, particularly those in which the angular discordance between beds above and below is slight, may extend over thousands of square miles. Such widespread unconformities necessarily must have been nearly horizontal. Structural deformation may be interpreted from variations in thickness of stratigraphic intervals beneath unconformities. A hypothetical example is shown in Figure 27.

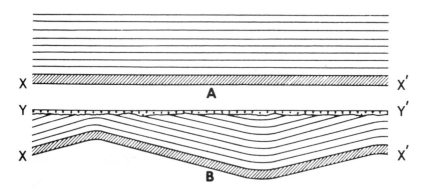

Figure 27. Hypothetical geologic sections illustrating how folding is shown by difference in thickness beneath an unconformity. Section A illustrates stratigraphic sequence prior to folding. Section B illustrates sequence after development of angular unconformity YY'. Difference in thickness between beds XX' and YY' is a measure of folding that occurred before development of unconformity YY' and after deposition of underlying beds. After Lee (1954).

Thickness Maps and Geologic Structure

Thickness variations portrayed on maps may be interpreted in the same manner as thickness variations shown in sections. Consider a contour map showing thickness variations (Figure 28). If the upper surface of the sedimentary unit whose thickness is represented is assumed to be horizontal, then the thickness contours may be regarded as showing the vertical distance from the horizontal upper surface to the deformed lower surface (Figure 28B). The thickness contours also may be considered to represent the structure of the lower surface at that moment in geologic time when the upper surface was formed. A structure contour map portrays differences in elevation of a stratigraphic horizon with respect to a datum, which is usually sea level. The horizon is usually the upper or lower surface of a bed, although the elevation of an unconformity can be represented. The use of contours on a structure

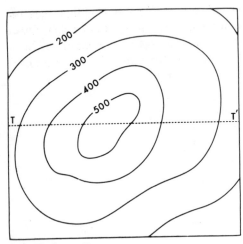

A. Thickness Map

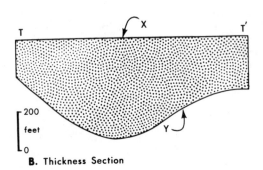

B. Thickness Section

Figure 28. (A) Thickness contour map and (B) corresponding geologic section TT' drawn so that upper surface, X, is horizontal. Contour map also may be interpreted as structure contour map which shows elevation of lower surface, Y, at time that upper surface was formed. If upper surface formed at sea level, configuration of lower surface could be shown with negative contour values representing distance below sea level.

contour map is analogous to their use in a topographic map except that the stratigraphic horizon represented by contours need not be exposed at the surface.

Sources of Error in Interpreting Thickness Maps and Sections

Preparation and interpretation of thickness maps and sections are not without hazards, particularly if the thickness data are obtained from well logs. One source of error results from faults penetrated in wells.

Normal faults result in erroneously small apparent thicknesses, and reverse faults in erroneously great apparent thicknesses (Figure 29). Commonly there is little or no direct indication of a fault penetrated by a single well. Consequently, faults in buried strata may be unrecognized

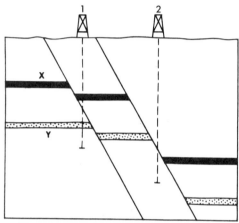

A. Normal Faults

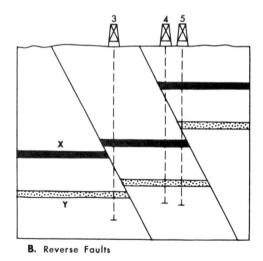

B. Reverse Faults

Figure 29. Geologic sections showing apparent variations in thickness due to faults. (A) Normal faults cause interval between beds X and Y to appear abnormally thin in well 1, and to be missing in well 2. (B) Reverse faults cause interval between beds X and Y to appear abnormally thick in well 3. In well 4, bed X is encountered twice, and in well 5, there is duplication of interval between beds X and Y.

unless logs of a number of relatively closely spaced wells are available for comparison.

Another source of error in interpreting thickness maps is lack of initial horizontality. Sedimentary strata are rarely deposited in a perfect horizontal position. Thus, an interpretation based on an assumption of initial horizontality will be in error by the amount that the beds deviated from the horizontal when deposited. A hypothetical example of an erroneous interpretation is shown in Figure 30. The upper surface of the sedimentary sequence is an unconformity representing a former land surface of considerable relief (Figure 30A). If the unconformity is plotted more or less horizontally, ignoring local irregularities, the resulting structural interpretation suggests the presence of broad folds (Figure 30B). In reality, however, the underlying beds should remain horizontal.

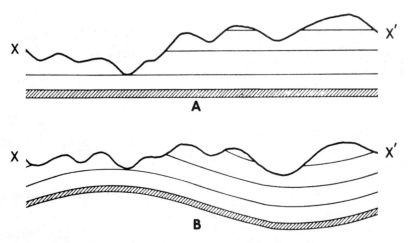

Figure 30. Hypothetical sections showing effect of erroneous assumption of initial horizontality. (A) Unconformity XX' reflects irregular former land surface. (B) Erroneous reconstruction resulting from plotting unconformity horizontally. Adapted from Lee (Kansas Geological Survey, 1954).

Alternative Interpretation

If differences in thickness of a sedimentary unit result from warping of the crust, thickness maps and sections of the unit as a whole will reveal only the total amount of warping that took place during the interval of time represented by difference in age of the lower and upper surfaces. The sequence of structural events may be revealed, however, if additional information is available. Figure 31 shows three hypothetical cross sections of a sedimentary unit in which the total thickness variations are identical. Strata represented in Figure 31A were warped after deposition of bed XX′ and before deposition of overlying sediments. The strata of Figure 31B, however, were deposited and then folded and eroded prior to deposition of bed YY′. The strata of Figure 31C were warped progressively while sedimentation occurred in the interval between XX′ and YY′.

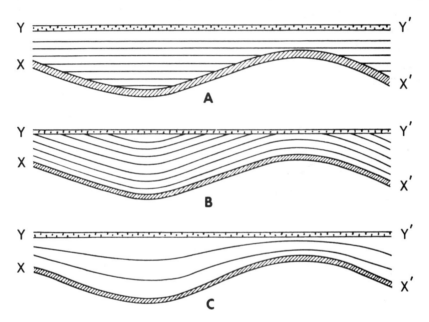

Figure 31. Geologic sections showing alternative sequences of geological events that pertain to same overall thickness interval. (A) Folding of XX′ followed by deposition of overlying beds. (B) Deposition of XX′ and all overlying beds except YY′, followed by folding, beveling and deposition of YY′. (C) Progressive folding during deposition of interval between XX′ and YY′. Adapted from Lee (Kansas Geological Survey, 1954).

PALEOGEOLOGIC MAPS

A paleogeologic map shows the areal distribution of geologic formations at a particular time in the past. A paleogeologic map is a geologic map of an ancient land surface. A modern geologic map portrays distribution of formations that crop out today, whereas a paleogeologic map portrays formations that cropped out on an ancient erosion surface.

A paleogeologic map generally shows the distribution of formations beneath an unconformity. The age of the unconformity governs the age of the map. Thus, if a paleogeologic map shows the distribution of formations beneath an unconformity which forms the base of the Pennsylvanian, the resulting map is a pre-Pennsylvanian paleogeologic map which shows the distribution of outcropping formations just *before* Pennsylvanian strata were deposited.

Paleogeologic maps are useful for interpreting the time of origin of structural features and sequence of events in the structural development of an area, particularly where the strata dip gently and may be correlated over long distances. Interpretation of their structure accords with interpretation of regular geologic maps. For example, an anticline is represented by an outcrop pattern in which the oldest unit is flanked by progressively younger units on either a geologic map (Figure 32A) or paleogeologic map (Figure 32B).

Paleogeologic maps may be constructed from information supplied by both geologic maps and boreholes (Figure 33). The objective is to map formations that occur directly beneath the unconformity serving as the map datum. When all available information has been assembled, the map may be constructed. In places a paleogeologic map may be relatively accurate; elsewhere, it may be highly interpretative because of scarcity of information.

INTERPRETING STRUCTURAL HISTORY

Thickness maps and paleogeologic maps are useful tools in combination with each other. They permit quantitative interpretation of

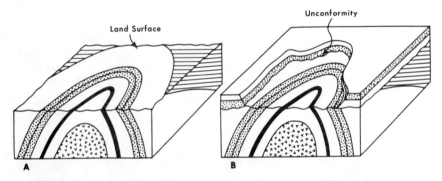

Figure 32. (A) Block diagram showing plunging anticline; upper surface of block may be regarded as geologic map. (B) Plunging anticline beneath unconformity; flat-lying beds above unconformity have been partly stripped away to show paleogeologic map.

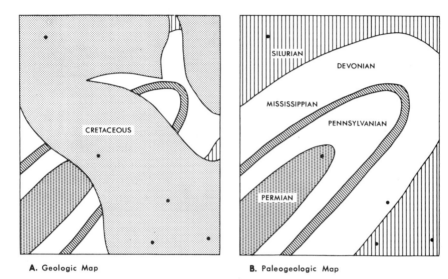

A. Geologic Map   **B.** Paleogeologic Map

Figure 33. (A) Geologic map showing Cretaceous strata resting uncon-
formably on folded Paleozoic strata. (B) Pre-Cretaceous paleogeologic
map based on information provided by geologic map, plus information
obtained from wells (shown by small black circles). Plunging syncline
involving Paleozoic strata was folded sometime after deposition of
Permian strata (youngest strata involved in folding) and before deposition of Cretaceous strata. Additional information would be needed to
narrow range of time of folding.

structural development of an area. To illustrate, maps and sections involving Paleozoic strata of the Forest City Basin of Kansas, Nebraska,
Iowa and Missouri, are shown in Figures 34 to 37. The Forest City
Basin extends over an area of about 50,000 square miles. The geology
of the area consists of a veneer of Paleozoic limestones, sandstones and
shales resting on Precambrian igneous and metamorphic rocks. From
early Paleozoic to present, the strata have been slowly and unevenly
warped.

The structure of the area in early Ordovician time is shown in
Figures 34 and 35. The pre-Middle Ordovician paleogeologic map
(Figure 34A) reveals the former presence of a broad, elongate anticline, the Nebraska Arch (Figure 34B), which brought Precambrian
rocks to the surface in Early Ordovician time. A thickness map of
combined Lower Ordovician and Upper Cambrian strata (Figure 34B)
reveals that about 2000 feet of warping took place between a gently
subsiding syncline toward the east (Ozark Basin) and the Nebraska
Arch toward the west.

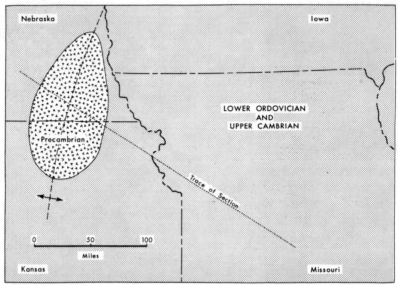

A. Pre-Middle Ordovician Paleogeologic Map

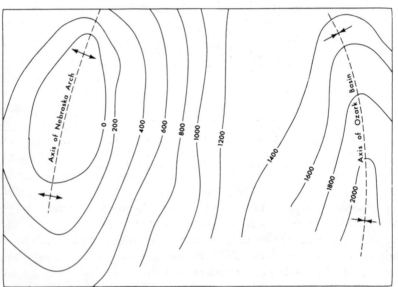

B. Thickness of Lower Ordovician and Upper Cambrian Rocks

Figure 34. Paleogeologic map and thickness map of area of present Forest City Basin. Maps portray geology existing immediately prior to middle part of Ordovician Period. Accompanying paleostructural section is shown in Figure 35A. Adapted from Lee (U. S. Geological Survey, 1946).

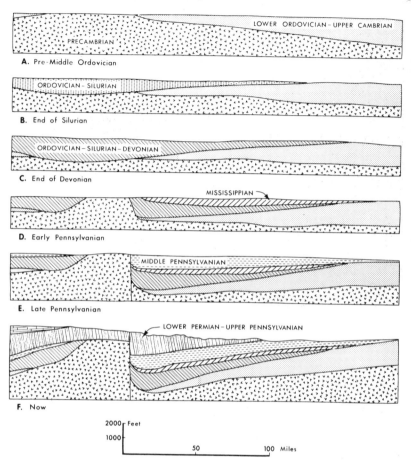

Figure 35. Series of geologic sections through Forest City Basin show-ing progressive structural development. Route of sections is shown in Figure 34A. Adapted from Lee (U. S. Geological Survey, 1946).

Structural changes during Silurian and the middle and latter part of Ordovician time witnessed almost complete reversal of upwarping and downwarping. The pre-Devonian paleogeologic map (Figure 36A) and cross section (Figure 35B) reveal a broad, northeast-southwest trending syncline in the northwestern part of the area formerly occupied by the Nebraska Arch. Thickness variations in combined Silurian and Upper and Middle Ordovician strata reveal (Figure 36B) that sharp downwarping occurred in a localized basin, the North Kansas Basin, within the broad syncline.

Later structural configuration is shown in Figure 35C to 35F and Figure 37. Downwarping continued in the North Kansas Basin during

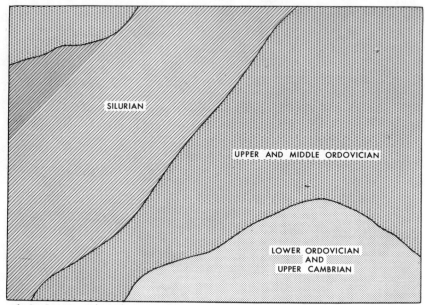

A. ·Pre-Devonian Paleogeologic Map

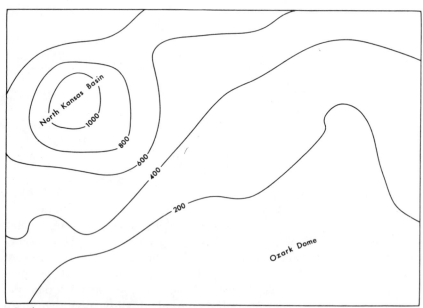

B. Thickness of Silurian and Upper and Middle Ordovician Rocks

Figure 36. (A) Pre-Devonian paleogeologic map of Forest City Basin. (B) Map of thickness of combined Silurian and Middle and Upper Ordovician strata. Adapted from Lee (U. S. Geological Survey, 1946).

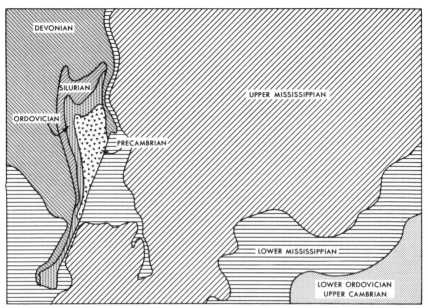

A. Pre-Pennsylvanian Paleogeologic Map

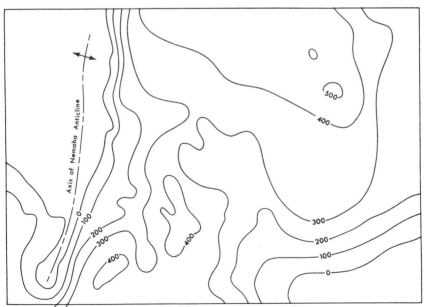

B. Thickness of Mississippian Rocks

Figure 37. (A) Pre-Pennsylvanian paleogeologic map of Forest City Basin. (B) Thickness map of Mississippian strata. Adapted from Lee (U. S. Geological Survey, 1946).

the Devonian (Figure 35C) and into most of the Mississippian. At the close of the Mississippian or the beginning of the Pennsylvanian Period, however, a dramatic change occurred. The former North Kansas Basin was transformed into a broad asymmetric, north-northeast trending anticline (Nemaha Anticline). The shape of the anticline is revealed by the pre-Pennsylvanian paleogeologic map (Figure 37A) and section (Figure 35D). Warping that occurred elsewhere in the Forest City Basin in the Mississippian and early in the Pennsylvanian is revealed by thickness variations in Mississippian rocks (Figure 37B). Subsequent evolutionary changes in the Forest City Basin include development, during Pennsylvanian time, of a fault bounding the Nemaha Anticline on its east side, and renewed slow uplift of the entire anticline continuing to the present (Figure 35E and F).

REFERENCES

BISHOP, MARGARET W., *Subsurface Mapping*. New York: John Wiley and Sons, 1960. (Chapter 7 deals with thickness maps.)

KING, P. B., *The Evolution of North America*. Princeton: Princeton University Press, 1959. (Chapter 3 deals with interpretation of thickness and paleogeologic maps.)

LEE, WALLACE, "Structural Development of the Forest City Basin, Missouri, Kansas, Iowa, and Nebraska," *U. S. Geological Survey Oil and Gas Invest.* No. 48, 1946.

LEE, WALLACE, "Thickness Maps as Criteria of Regional Structural Movement," *Kansas Geological Survey Bulletin*, 109, 65-80, 1954.

LEVORSEN, A. I., *Paleogeologic Maps*. San Francisco: W. H. Freeman and Company, 1960. (Provides thorough treatment of preparation and interpretation of paleogeologic maps.)

MOORE, C. A., *Handbook of Subsurface Geology*. New York: Harper & Row, 1963. (Chapter 1 deals with interpretation of structure contour maps; Chapter 3 deals with thickness maps.)

SUMMARY OUTLINE

Interpretation of thickness maps
> Evidence for ancient structural deformation
> Assumption of initial horizontality
> Effect of faults on apparent thickness
> Alternative interpretations

Paleogeologic maps and "modern" geologic maps

Construction of paleogeologic maps

Interpretation of paleogeologic maps

Relation of paleogeologic and thickness maps

CHAPTER

5

Sedimentary Facies

TOPICS

Concept of facies
Lithofacies and biofacies
Mississippi River delta complex

Environmental factors
Reef complexes

INTRODUCTION

Early geologists who studied stratified rocks regarded each layer as a feature that persisted laterally without change. According to this view, each layer was deposited in a "Universal Ocean." With rise of the doctrine of uniformitarianism, there was gradual decline of insistence that layered rocks do not change laterally. Today, of course, we realize that most, if not all, strata vary laterally. These varying aspects of rocks may be termed *facies,* and the concept of lateral variation in bodies of rock is the *facies concept.* In spite of the simplicity of this concept, its full significance is still being developed.

The persistence of older ideas and their influence on interpretation is illustrated by evolution of ideas pertaining to the origin and relationships of beds in Middle and Upper Devonian strata of New York State and adjacent Pennsylvania. These rocks provide one of the most carefully studied examples of facies changes in the world. The strata dip gently southward and may be traced for more than 300 miles in an east-west outcrop belt. Beds in the lower part of the sequence consist of fossiliferous limestones and dark shales, which are succeeded upward by sandy shales. Great thicknesses of red and gray siltstones and sandstones, termed the Catskill Group, form the upper part of the sequence.

Until the 1920's, the Catskill deposits were presumed to be stratigraphically higher than other beds in the sequence (Figure 38A). Renewed study beginning in the 1920's, however, suggested that the facies concept had been much too cautiously applied previously, and that the Catskill deposits were actually the stratigraphic equivalents (Figure 38B) of other deposits that had formerly been assumed to lie stratigraphically beneath the Catskill deposits. The later interpretation accords well with ideas pertaining to depositional environments applied elsewhere. According to this view, the Catskill deposits record the growth of a large deltaic complex fed by streams that carried sediment from long-persisting mountains that lay to the east. The deltaic complex advanced slowly westward, encroaching on a shallow, open sea which covered large areas in the continental interior. Thus, the different facies of the Devonian strata reflect both differences in types of sediment deposited and different environmental conditions. While streams were depositing red sands and silts on floodplains in what is now eastern New York State, limestone and shale were being deposited under quiet water conditions to the west.

Definition of Facies

The term facies pertains to the variable aspects of bodies of rock. As such, the term is applicable to any type of rock. For example, a

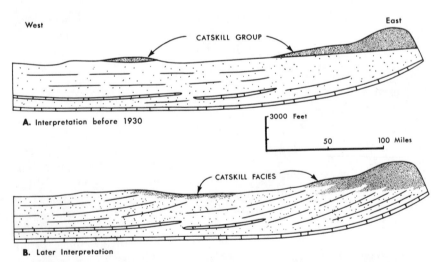

Figure 38. East-west geologic sections through Middle and Upper Devonian strata in New York State. (A) Interpretation of stratigraphic relationships until the 1920's; (B) Present interpretation. Gently curving lines represent time planes which cut across facies boundaries. Adapted from C. O. Dunbar and J. W. Rodgers, **Principles of Stratigraphy,** with permission of John Wiley & Sons, Inc.

granitic pluton may be composed of different types of granite in different places. These differing components may be regarded as facies of the pluton. Since we are concerned with sedimentary rocks, a generalized definition of sedimentary facies framed by Raymond C. Moore (1949) is appropriate: "Sedimentary facies are areally segregated parts of different nature belonging to any genetically related body of sedimentary deposits." This definition does not specify the types of variation. If we wish, we can specify facies that are concerned solely with the physical aspects of lithology, including mineralogy, grain size, color and bedding. These aspects may be termed *lithofacies*. On the other hand, facies may pertain to aspects that are largely biological or paleontological, or in other words, *biofacies* aspects.

Given these rather general concepts of facies, it is obvious that different kinds of facies can be distinguished within a given formation. For example, various lithofacies distinguished on the basis of mineral composition in a dolomitic limestone formation may be quite different than biofacies defined by assemblages of fossils. Complications arise because clean-cut distinctions between lithofacies and biofacies aspects can rarely be made. The biological components of sedimentary rocks are also physical components. For example, some limestone formations are composed almost entirely of fragments of fossils. Thus, aspects of mineralogy, grain size and bedding also reflect differences in biological materials. Some geologists suggest that the term lithofacies should pertain to all aspects of lithology, including those of biological origin.

Many problems of sedimentary facies are semantic in that they stem from difficulties of classifying features that vary more or less continuously. There is long-standing desire to devise classification systems capable of representing and describing sedimentary facies. Unfortunately, no universally satisfactory classification system has been developed and it seems probable that none will be developed. The use of contour maps to portray continuously varying proportions of lithological or paleontological constituents avoids some of the difficulties that arise when rigid "pigeonhole" classification methods are employed. Examples of contoured facies maps are provided by Sloss, Dapples and Krumbein (1960).

Environmental Factors

Different sedimentary facies form because different sedimentary materials are supplied to sites of deposition and because there are differences in environment of deposition from place to place. An objective of stratigraphy is to interpret the origin of sedimentary facies in terms of materials supplied and environment of deposition. Correct inter-

pretation of environment of deposition may be critical if the age relationships of different facies are to be properly established, as for example,
in the Catskill deposits of New York State (Figure 38). This objective
is perhaps the most dynamic and challenging of all in stratigraphy,
requiring close liaison with biology, paleontology, sedimentology, mineralogy, geochemistry and paleoecology (Figure 1).

Paleoecology is closely linked with interpretation of sedimentary
facies. Modern ecology is concerned with the mutual interrelationships
between organisms and their environments; paleoecology is concerned
with ancient organisms and their environments. Most of the knowledge
of ancient organisms and their environments is obtained from assemblages of fossils and the strata in which they are contained. There are
important differences, however, between assemblages of fossils and com-
munities of living organisms. Assemblages of fossils may provide only
an incomplete and distorted representation of the organisms that lived
at the locality at which the strata containing the fossils was deposited.
One reason is that only organisms with hard parts are commonly preserved as fossils; the fossil record of soft-bodied organisms is quite
scant by comparison. Secondly, unless the fossil organisms are preserved where they lived, as for example, corals and calcareous algae
preserved in position of growth, the assemblage of fossils may represent
a mixture of organisms derived from different environments and brought
together by waves and currents after death. In spite of its shortcomings,
the fossil record is marvelously rich and paleoecology is still in infancy,
having yet to take full advantage of the storehouse of information po-
tentially available.

Most sedimentary strata were deposited in water. Thus, interpretation of ancient depositional environments is largely a matter of interpreting conditions that prevailed in ancient bodies of water. Table 5
provides a summary of the principal kinds of evidence that bear on
major aqueous environmental factors, including both physical and biological forms of evidence.

EXAMPLES OF FACIES RELATIONSHIPS

A large number of facies relationships could be considered. In subsequent pages, examples are provided of (1) facies related to organic
reefs and (2) facies related to river deltas; both types provide oppor-
tunity for application of the facies concept.

Many sedimentary facies relationships can be interpreted in terms
of change of sea level with respect to land. Rising sea level results in
transgression of the sea over the land, whereas falling sea level results
in regression of the sea. The sequence of deposits formed under the two

conditions have important differences. Deposits formed nearshore generally differ from those formed offshore. Thus, deposits produced in response to rising sea level tend to record progressive migration of facies in a landward direction, producing an *onlapping* facies relationship (Figure 39A). On the other hand, deposits formed in a regressing sea tend to exhibit an *offlapping* facies relationship (Figure 39B).

Organic reefs generally exhibit complex facies relationships. Organic reefs are produced by calcium carbonate secreting organisms that create wave-resistant masses of rock in relatively shallow water marine conditions. Modern examples include the Great Barrier Reef of Australia, and the atoll reefs of the Pacific, such as Bikini Atoll. Many examples of ancient reefs, ranging in age from Precambrian to modern, are preserved in the stratigraphic record. Reef-building organisms are highly varied, and include corals, calcareous algae, sponges, brachiopods, pelecypods and foraminifers. Only part of the volume of a reef complex is produced directly by reef-builders. The greatest volume of sedimentary rock tends to be formed in lagoons toward the lee side of reefs and on submarine slopes on the seaward side of reefs. Environmental variations on the two sides of a reef tend to have strong influence on the character of sediments deposited, for large variations in depth, water temperature, dissolved solids, and turbulence may occur within relatively short distances.

Guadalupian Reef Complex

The Guadalupian reef complex, of Permian age, provides an excellent example of diverse facies formed under marine conditions. Although the reef complex crops out in the Guadalupe Mountains of West Texas and adjacent southeastern New Mexico, most of the complex is buried and is known from oil-well drilling operations. The reef itself forms an arc-like pattern that has been traced for more than 400 miles (Figure 40).

Deposition of the reef complex was strongly influenced by the living reef which, at times, served as a boundary between a relatively deep basin and a broad shelf (Figure 41). Deposits formed in shallow lagoons which lay between the reef and land areas, consist of flat-lying limestones that grade laterally into anhydrite beds, and subsequently into reddish siltstones and sandstones. On the seaward side of the reef, reef talus deposits were formed on steep slopes that extended to depths of 2000 feet or more. The slope deposits grade laterally into flat-lying deposits formed on the floor of a deep basin.

Understanding of facies relationships in the Guadalupian reef complex is essential for correct interpretation of age relationships. The gross facies relationships are explained by offlapping deposits formed in a

TABLE 5

Major types of evidence that bear on interpretation of aqueous depositional environments.

Environmental Factor	Type of Evidence			
	Stratigraphic	Sedimentological	Paleontological and Biological	Chemical
Salinity of water	(1) Presence of soil zones and stream channel deposits suggests deposition under fresh-water conditions.	(1) Presence of coal and lignite beds indicates deposition under brackish or fresh-water swamp conditions.	(1) Aquatic animals and plants preserved as fossils and whose affinities to living forms are known provide strong evidence. For example, modern corals live in sea water; therefore, fossil corals preserved in growth position indicate that deposits formed in sea water. Transportation of organisms after death may invalidate their use as salinity indicators.	(1) Presence of salt water in pores of sedimentary rocks indicates deposition in salt water.
Depth of water	(1) Presence of scour channels suggests shallow depths, not exceeding a few tens of feet. Important exceptions are submarine canyons and deep channels on continental shelves. (2) Geometrical relationships of different facies: For example, certain reef facies formed at shallow depths pass laterally into slope facies and then to deep-basin facies.	(1) Presence of coal and lignite beds suggests depths of only a few feet. (2) Presence of mud-cracks and raindrop imprints indicates exposure to atmosphere, in turn, suggesting fluctuating, very shallow depths.	(1) Presence of fossil algae: Algae require light; therefore algae could not have lived at depths where light intensity was low. (2) Presence of assemblages of fossils whose modern counterparts live in shallow water.	
Water temperature	(1) Presence of evaporite (gypsum, anhydrite, halite) beds suggests warm air and water conditions which promoted evaporation.		(1) Assemblages of fossils: For example, most modern corals live in tropical or subtropical sea. Thus, most ancient corals are presumed to have lived in warm waters.	(1) Temperature of water in which calcium carbonate is precipitated or is secreted by organisms affects ratio of the isotopes oxygen-18/oxygen-16. Ancient water temperatures can be calculated on the basis of extremely accurate measurements of oxygen isotope ratios in calcareous algae, and in calcium carbonate shells.

Water temperature (con't)			(2)Solubility of calcium carbonate decreases with increasing temperature; thus, limestones generally imply deposition in warm water.
Turbulence of water	(1) Reef deposits suggest turbulent shallow water. (2)Presence of scour channels suggests high turbulence. (3)Presence of irregular cross-bedding in coarse sediments suggests turbulence.	(1)Presence of sand-sized or larger particles that are well sorted and are rounded due to abrasion, suggest deposition under turbulent condition. (2)Presence of oolites and other spherical particles of calcium carbonate suggest turbulence.	(1) Animals with massive skeletons (corals, thick-shelled pelecypods and brachiopods) suggest turbulent conditions. (2)Delicate rigid skeletons suggest relatively quiet water conditions. (3)Flexible skeletons (leathery algae, sea whips) suggest turbulence.
Cloudiness or turbidity of water		(1)Presence of mud and silt-sized particles in sediments indicates that the water near the bottom must have been cloudy or at least, intermittently cloudy.	(1)Presence of fossil algae indicates that water was sufficiently clear to permit light to penetrate to growth sites of algae. (2)Presence of marine animals that prefer clear water, such as corals, suggests relative clarity of water.
Consolidation of sediment on seafloor		(1)Presence of sole markings, flow rolls, flute casts, and other small-scale sedimentary structures indicates that bottom sediment was poorly consolidated when initially deposited.	(1)Presence of "fossil" burrows made by worms or clams indicates initially soft bottom sediment. (2)Presence of hard "pavement-forming" carbonate-secreting organisms (such as certain algae) indicates firm sea floor.
Nearness of land	(1)Lateral changes from marine facies to nonmarine facies.	(1)Grain size of sediment may be a measure of proximity to land, coarser sizes tending to occur nearer to land.	(1)Presence of leaves, twigs, wood, or bark in marine sediments suggests former proximity to land, although plant material can be carried to sea for substantial distances. (2)Progressive change in fossil assemblages may indicate transition from shallow to deep water marine environments.

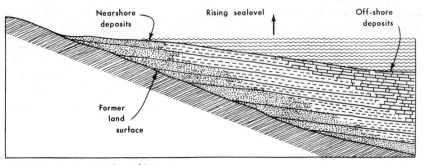

A. Onlapping Facies Relationship

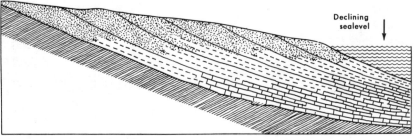

B. Offlapping Facies Relationship

Figure 39. Generalized facies relationships resulting from (A) transgression of the sea and from (B) regression of the sea.

Figure 40. Map showing ancient geography of West Texas and southeastern New Mexico at close of Middle Permian time. (1) Deep basin in which sandstones and dark siltstones accumulated; (2) living reef; (3) back-reef lagoonal areas in which limestones were deposited; (4) area of intermittent flooding in which limestone, anhydrite, salt and red siltstones and sandstones were deposited; (5) lowland area in which sandy and shaly red beds were deposited. Adapted from King (U. S. Geological Survey, 1948).

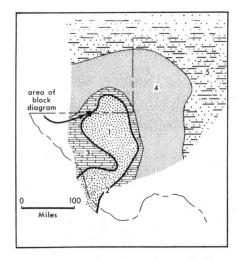

slowly regressing sea. Evidence is provided by progressive encroachment of reef facies over beds of reef talus (Figure 41). The reef facies consists of massive limestone created by sponges and calcareous algae. The talus deposits, however, consist largely of fragmental material derived from the reef and subsequently transported down submarine slopes to create curving, fan-like wedges of poorly sorted debris composed of particles ranging from small grains to blocks weighing many tons. The

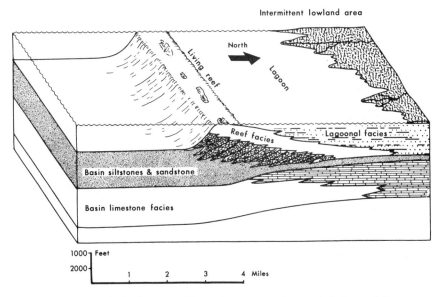

Figure 41. Block diagram illustrating geography and facies relationships of Guadalupian reef complex at close of Middle Permian time. Geographic location of block is shown in Figure 40. Adapted from King (U. S. Geological Survey, 1948).

talus deposits, in turn, pass laterally into sandstones and dark siltstones and thin-bedded limestones deposited under stagnant-water conditions in the deep basin. The geometry of the deposits permits ancient water depths to be estimated. Beds formed simultaneously within short lateral distances from each other were deposited at depths that differed as much as 2000 feet. Strictly applied, the law of initial horizontality would be quite misleading under these circumstances and would tend to obscure the relationships that are readily explained by a deep basin and an adjacent shallow-water reef and shelf.

The thousands of feet of shallow marine deposits that form part of the Guadalupian reef complex indicate that there was long-continued downwarping of the earth's crust. The offlapping relationship with progressive migration of facies can be explained by assuming that accumulation of sediment kept pace with, or exceeded the rate of subsidence, causing the reef to form outward and over previously formed talus deposits.

Thornton Reef Complex

A reef complex of Silurian age exposed at Thornton, Illinois, just south of Chicago, provides a good example of the close relationships between lithofacies and biofacies, and their importance in the interpretation of depositional environments. The general configuration of the Thornton complex is illustrated by the cross section of Figure 42. The flanks of the reef complex consist of steeply dipping beds of dolomitic limestone that grade laterally into massive limestones of the reef core. More detailed lithologic facies are represented in the map of Figure 43.

Figure 42. Cross section AA' through Silurian reef complex at Thornton, Illinois, showing reef-core deposits (solid black) and reef-flank deposits. Route of section is shown in Figure 43. Adapted from Jerome J. C. Ingels, "Geometry, Paleontology, and Petrography of Thornton Reef Complex, Silurian of Northeastern Illinois," **A. A. P. G. Bulletin** 47:405-440, March, 1963, with permission of American Association of Petroleum Geologists.

Lithologic facies distinguished in the Thornton complex are closely related to biofacies (Figure 44) distinguished on the basis of predominant fossil organism types. The relative abundance of fossil organisms within different biofacies varies in a regular manner with respect to geographic position (Figure 45). The biofacies may be separated into two general classes, those occurring in the reef core, and those occurring in the reef flank. Principal constituents of the biofacies are listed in Table 6.

The spatial distribution of lithofacies and biofacies in the Thornton reef complex enables the environments of deposition to be interpreted. From southwest to northeast, the following depositional environments may be distinguished (Figure 46): (1) An outer reef front, which received the main force of waves which broke against the reef, existed on the southwest side of the complex. The predominant wind direction is interpreted as having been from the southwest. This environment is now represented by coraliferous dolomite (Figure 43) and by the coral biofacies (Figure 44). The large corals, in conjunction with stromatoporoids that encrusted them, and the abundance of fragmental debris in the coral biofacies, suggest that highly turbulent water conditions existed at the edge of the reef. An outer ridge of stromatoporoids is

Figure 43. Lithofacies map of Thornton reef complex: (1) coraliferous dolomite, (2) cyclically bedded fossiliferous dolomite, (3) non-bedded crinoidal dolomite, (4) well-bedded crinoidal dolomite, (5) cyclically bedded poorly fossiliferous dolomite, (6) alternating beds of dolomite and clay, and (7) silt and clay-rich dolomite. Dashed line is trace of sections shown in Figures 42 and 45. Adapted from Ingels (1963) with permission of the American Association of Petroleum Geologists.

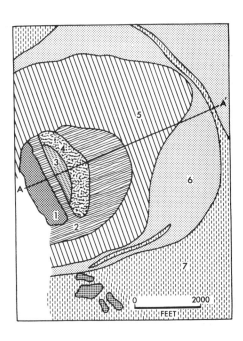

thought to have received the initial brunt of the waves and was succeeded inwardly by a wave-resisting rampart of living corals. (2) Directly behind the coral rampart, there was a "dead reef flat" in which environmental conditions favored trilobites, the presence of numerous unbroken trilobite specimens suggesting that water turbulence was less than in the outer reef front. Lack of fine fragmental debris, however, suggests that there was some turbulence. (3) The next environmental zone is a former beach that formed at the edge of a lagoon, directly in back of the dead reef flat. The lagoonal beach environment is now represented by the cyclically bedded fossiliferous dolomite lithofacies (Figure 43), which contains abundant fragmental debris in places. Cephalopods flourished in the lagoonal beach environment, their abundant remains creating the cephalopod biofacies (Figure 44). (4) Next toward the northeast there was a shallow lagoonal crinoidal "meadow"

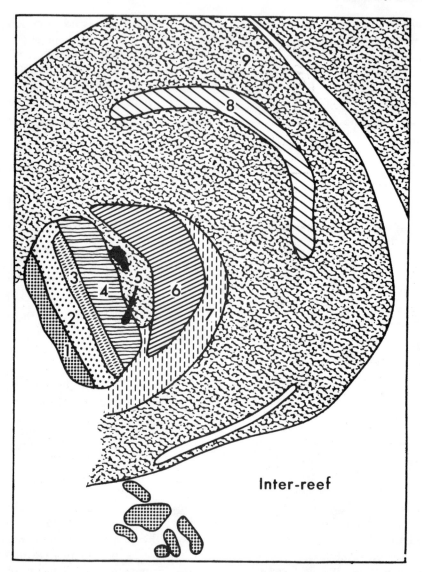

Figure 44. Biofacies map of Thornton reef complex: (1) coral biofacies, (2) trilobite biofacies, (3) cephalopod biofacies, (4) crinoid biofacies, (5) stromatoporoid biofacies, (6) pentamerid brachiopod biofacies, (7) gastropod biofacies, (8) sponge biofacies, and (9) heterogeneous biofacies. Characteristics of biofacies are listed in Table 6. Diagram showing generalized variations in proportions of different organisms along line of cross section AA' (Figure 43) is shown in Figure 45. Biofacies are not distinguished in inter-reef areas. Adapted from Ingels (1963) with permission of the American Association of Petroleum Geologists.

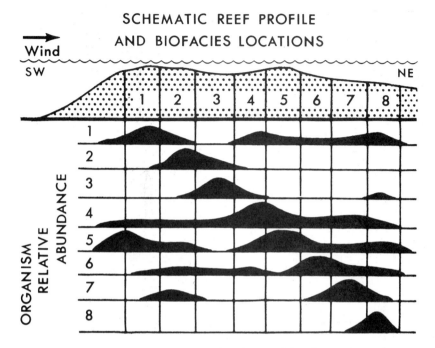

Figure 45. Variations in relative abundance of fossil organisms along line of cross section AA' (Figure 43) through Thornton reef complex: (1) coral abundance and coral biofacies, (2) trilobite abundance and trilobite biofacies, (3) cephalopod abundance and cephalopod biofacies, (4) crinoid abundance and crinoid biofacies, (5) stromatoporoid abundance and stromatoporoid biofacies, (6) pentamerid brachiopod abundance and pentamerid biofacies, (7) gastropod abundance and gastropod biofacies, (8) sponge abundance and sponge biofacies. Profile in upper part of drawing indicates generalized interpretation of water depths. Adapted from Ingels (1963) with permission of the American Association of Petroleum Geologists.

in which quiet water conditions generally prevailed, although occasional high tides and storm waves may have induced high turbulence intermittently. Crinoids flourished in the lagoon, accompanied by scattered colonies of corals and stromatoporoids. (5) The lee side of the reef was formed by a stromatoporoid ridge which served as a wave-resistant mass that completed the encirclement of the lagoon. (6) Moving still farther northeast, in water that was progressively deeper, brachiopods flourished, forming the brachiopod biofacies. Here, the environment was that of a continuously submerged bank, partly sheltered from vigorous wave action by the adjacent reef, but still experiencing some turbulence. (7) Progressively increasing depth, accompanied by increasing distances

TABLE 6

Constituents of biofacies types in Thornton reef complex. Geographic distribution of biofacies is shown in Figures 44 and 45.

Biofacies Types Occurring in Reef Core	Biofacies Types Occurring in Reef Flank
(1) Coral biofacies: Predominance of corals of both the colonial and solitary types; gastropods, brachiopods, trilobites, and some stromatoporoids also occur.	(5) Stromatoporoid biofacies: Massive rock-forming stromatoporoid colonies.
(2) Trilobite biofacies: Local aggregations of trilobite Bumastus; stromatoporoids and scattered individual gastropods are also present.	(6) Pentamerid brachiopod biofacies: Abundant pentamerid brachiopods; gastropods and stromatoporoids also occur.
(3) Cephalopod biofacies: Straight-coned cephalopods; trilobite Archtinurus is also abundant.	(7) Gastropod biofacies: Abundant gastropods, although corals and brachiopods are also present.
	(8) Sponge biofacies: Rock composed largely of the sponge Calathium, with stromatoporoids filling space between sponges.
(4) Crinoid biofacies: High proportion of crinoid stems in growth positions; corals and stromatoporoids are also present.	(9) Heterogeneous biofacies: Contains faunal elements characteristic of other biofacies but lacks a dominant faunal element.

from the reef, witnessed a change in environmental conditions in which gastropods flourished (gastropod biofacies), (8) a sponge biofacies formed and (9) finally, an environmental zone in which the bottom dwellers were mixed faunas (now represented by the heterogenous biofacies) formed that occupied the submerged bank at progressively increasing depths.

In summary, the Thornton reef complex provides a good example of the interrelationships between lithofacies and biofacies, and the use of information derived from both types of facies in interpreting ancient environments.

Mississippi River Delta Complex

Sedimentary deposits formed by river deltas also provide examples of facies variations. The delta complex formed by the Mississippi River is one of the best known deltaic sequences in the world. The Mississippi delta, in company with other deltas, records the interplay between a river's attempts to extend its embankments seaward, and the sea's attempts to destroy the delta through erosion.

The modern delta of the Mississippi River (Figure 47) is less than 500 years old. It, plus earlier deltas which form part of a deltaic com-

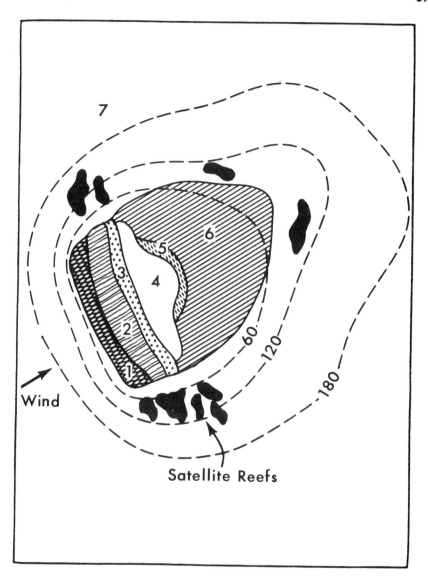

Figure 46. Map of inferred depositional environments during deposition of Thornton reef complex when it had been built up roughly 300 feet above its base: (1) outer reef front consisting of stromatoporoid ridge and coral rampart, (2) dead reef flat, (3) lagoon beach, (4) lagoonal crinoid meadow, (5) leeward stromatoporoidal ridge, (6) back-reef bank occupied principally by gastropods, and (7) deeper parts of bank surrounding the reef which were occupied by mixed faunas. Contour lines pertain to estimated water depths in feet. Adapted from Ingels (1963) with permission of the American Association of Petroleum Geologists.

plex, was formed by the large volume of sediment brought to and dumped in the Gulf of Mexico by the Mississippi River. The area drained by the Mississippi River and its tributaries spans about 40 percent of the area of the United States (excluding Alaska and Hawaii), and part of southern Canada. As the Mississippi River enters its present delta, it splits into a number of major distributaries, which in turn, are further subdivided into lesser distributaries. The river enters the Gulf of Mexico around much of the delta's perimeter. The present

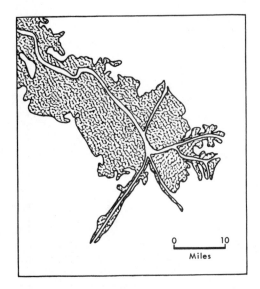

0   10

Miles

Figure 47. Map of Mississippi delta.

Mississippi delta may be considered to be a compound delta, composed of an aggregate of individual lesser deltas created by the principal distributaries.

Variations in type of sediments, plus the gross geometry, provide evidence bearing on growth and development of the Mississippi's present delta. Figure 48A shows a simplified and idealized vertical profile through the Mississippi delta. The upper surface of the delta slopes seaward to depths of 6 to 10 feet, at which point the slope increases until it flattens out again further seaward. Figure 48B portrays variations in sediment size distribution. Near shore, sand and silt-sized material predominates, whereas clay increases seaward. Farther seaward, however, clay content declines and the proportion of sand increases, reflecting the presence of sandy sediments on the shelf that underlies the Gulf of Mexico. Sediment-size variations are related to sediment source materials (Figure 48C). River sand predominates shoreward, whereas marine sand, land-plant material, and sand-sized shell material predominates seaward.

These differences in sediment characteristics and in gross geometry reflect differences in sedimentary environments. Figure 49 shows the areal distribution of the four general environmental types at the mouth of the Mississippi's delta: (1) the pro-delta zone representing the relatively steeply sloping edge of the delta; (2) the delta front, representing the shallow flat-bottomed area at the front of the delta; (3) the delta

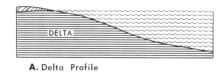

A. Delta Profile

B. Composition Total Sediment

C. Composition Sand-sized Sediment

Figure 48. Series of diagrams showing relationships between (A) profile of Mississippi delta, (B) composition of total sediment, and (C) source composition of sand-sized sediment. Adapted from P. C. Scruton, "Delta Building and the Deltaic Sequence," **A. A. P. G. Symposium Volume: Recent Sediments, Northwest Gulf of Mexico,** p. 82-102, with permission of the American Association of Petroleum Geologists.

Figure 49. Map showing principal depositional environments at south end of Mississippi delta. Adapted from H. N. Fisk, "Bar-finger sands of Mississippi Delta," **A. A. P. G. Symposium Volume: Geometry of Sandstone Bodies,** p. 29-52, with permission of the American Association of Petroleum Geologists.

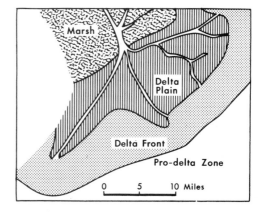

plain consisting of newly formed land created as the delta advances seaward and (4) the marsh environment which merges somewhat irregularly with the delta front.

The influences these different environments have on deposition are illustrated in the profile of Figure 50. Silty clay deposited in the prodelta zone forms seaward-dipping beds that are steeper than adjacent deposits formed either offshore or on the delta front or in marshes. "Time lines" in Figure 50 are outlines of former sediment surfaces. Each time line represents the configuration of the surface of the deposits at a particular instant in time. Considered in three-dimensions, the time lines are the traces on the vertical section where it intersects

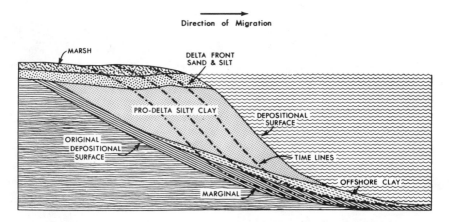

Figure 50. Idealized profile through delta migrating toward sea, showing configuration of time lines with respect to deposits formed under different environmental conditions. Adapted from Scruton (1960) with permission of American Association of Petroleum Geologists.

the former sediment surfaces. The time lines flatten landward, where they pass into deposits formed in the delta front, delta plain, and marsh environments.

When deposits formed by an individual distributary within the Mississippi delta are considered in greater detail, a number of lesser facies may be distinguished. The different facies represent, in part, deposits formed successively through time. Facies associated with a distributary are shown in Figure 51. In cross section, they consist of lenticular masses of sand and silty sand. The masses are elongate, parallel to the distributary, forming a "bar finger" deposit. The sands

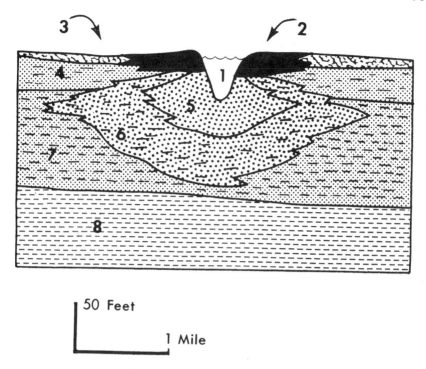

50 Feet

1 Mile

Figure 51. Cross section showing facies associated with distributary of Mississippi River: (1) distributary channel, (2) natural levee consisting of silty sands and silty clays, (3) organic-rich silty clays formed in marshes, (4) silty clays and silty sands deposited on delta plain, (5) zone of relatively clean sand within bar-finger deposit, (6) transition zone consisting of silty clays, (7) delta-front clay deposits, and (8) pro-delta deposits consisting of clay and silt. Adapted from Fisk (1961) with permission of the American Association of Petroleum Geologists.

of the bar finger are succeeded upward by clays and silty sands that form natural levees, which in turn, grade laterally to organic-rich clays formed in marshes.

The importance of recognizing different facies in a delta complex is emphasized by the development of Mississippi's alluvial plain in coastal Louisiana. The present geographic features (Figure 52) represent a complex of seven individual deltas that formed, one after another, in the past 5000 years. The individual deltas imbricate in shinglelike fashion, each younger delta having built upon and extended outward from its immediate predecessor. The arrangement of facies within each delta permits it to be distinguished from its neighbors.

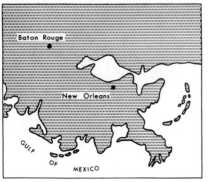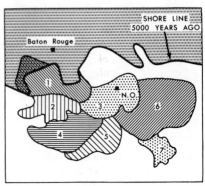

A. Present Shore Line   **B.** Sequence of Deltas

Figure 52. Alluvial plain in coastal Louisiana consisting of seven imbricating deltas formed in last 5000 years. Numbers denote sequence of ages of individual deltas; 1 is oldest and 7 is youngest, representing the present delta. Adapted from Scruton (1960) with permission of the American Association of Petroleum Geologists.

REFERENCES

DUNBAR, C. O. and RODGERS, J. W., *Principles of Stratigraphy.* New York: John Wiley and Sons, 1957.

FISK, H. N., "Bar-Finger Sands of the Mississippi Delta," in *Geometry of Sandstone Bodies,* Tulsa: Amer. Assn. Petroleum Geologists: 29-52.

HEDGPETH, J. W., ed., "Ecology" in *Treatise on Marine Ecology and Paleoecology,* from the *Geol. Soc. America Memoir 67:* Vol. 1, 1957. (Monumental work dealing with numerous aspects of marine ecology and environmental analysis.)

INGELS, J. J. C., "Geometry, Paleontology and Petrography of Thornton Reef Complex, Silurian of Northeastern Illinois," *Bull. Amer. Assn. of Petroleum Geologists,* 47: 405-440, 1963.

KING, P. B., Geology of the Southern Guadalupe Mountains, Texas. *U. S. Geological Survey Professional Paper 215,* 1948.

LADD, H. W., ed., "Paleoecology", in *Treatise on Marine Ecology and Paleoecology,* from the *Geol. Soc. America Memoir 67,* Vol. 2, 1957. (Treats principles and examples of paleocology.)

MOORE, R. C., "Meaning of Facies" in *Sedimentary Facies in Geological History,* from the *Geol. Soc. America Memoir 39,* 1949. (This and other articles in this volume deal with problems of facies nomenclature, classification and interpretation.

SCRUTON, P. C., "Delta Building and the Deltaic Sequence," in *Recent Sediments, Northwest Gulf of Mexico.* Tulsa: Amer. Assn. Petroleum Geologists: pp. 82-102, 1960.

SLOSS, L. L., DAPPLES, E. C., and KRUMBEIN, W. C., *Lithofacies Maps: An Atlas of the United States and Southern Canada.* New York: John Wiley and Sons, 1960. (Contains numerous examples of quantitative lithofacies maps.)

SUMMARY OUTLINE

The facies concept
Influence on interpretation of age relationships

Aspects of facies
Lithofacies and biofacies

Influence of environmental factors on facies
Types of evidence that bear on interpretation of ancient aqueous environments
Water salinity, depth, temperature, turbulence, turbidity, consolidation of sea floor
Nearness of land

Examples of facies relationships
Onlapping versus offlapping facies relationships
Guadalupian reef complex and Thornton reef complex
Mississippi River delta complex

6

Radiometric Age Dating

TOPICS

Nature of atoms
Electrons, protons and neutrons
Atomic number
Mass number
Spontaneous disintegration

Particles produced in radioactive decay
Uncertainty and probability
Law of radioactive decay
Decay clocks
Accumulation clocks

Quantitative geologic time scale

INTRODUCTION

Virtually all quantitative determinations of geologic age are based on radioactivity. By radioactivity, we mean the property of certain species of atoms, or nuclides, to emit or radiate particles and rays as a result of spontaneous breakdown of individual atoms. When an atom breaks down or decays, it is transformed into a daughter nuclide. The rate at which a given radioactive nuclide decays does not vary, although different radioactive nuclides decay at different rates. Some decay rapidly, some very slowly.

Determination of geologic age is made possible by the fact that a given radioactive nuclide decays at a uniform rate, and thus, forms a kind of geologic clock. It seems reasonable that rates of decay of various radioactive nuclides have remained virtually constant in the geologic past. This assumption is supported by experiments. Radioactive substances have been subjected to wide ranges in temperatures and pressures, to strong magnetic fields, to variations in chemical combination, and to bombardment with cosmic and other forms of radiation all with little effect in changing the rate of radioactive decay. These changes in environment of radioactive substances have little effect because the energy changes that they bring about are very small in proportion to the energy involved in radioactive decay.

In theory, any radioactive nuclide can be used as a radioactive clock unless it decays so slowly that its decay products cannot be measured, or its decay rate is too rapid to be useful. Since the decay rates of various radioactive nuclides differ, different nuclides may be employed in various geological age dating applications, depending on the chemical composition of minerals to be dated and their general geologic age. Fast-decaying nuclides are useful for dating relatively young materials; slow-decaying nuclides for relatively old materials.

NATURE OF ATOMS

Before discussing the determination of geologic age by radioactivity, it will be useful to review the general properties of atoms. An atom is the basic unit of the chemical elements. It was originally supposed that the atom was the smallest unit of matter and could not be divided further. It is common knowledge now, however, that atoms consist of still smaller particles.

In 1911 Rutherford, a British physicist, proposed that each atom consists of a small, positively charged nucleus that contains most of the mass of the atom, surrounded by a number of negatively charged electrons. Subsequently, the nucleus was shown to be composed of two principal kinds of particles: protons, which possess a postive electrical charge, and neutrons, which possess no charge, being electrically neutral. The overall electrical neutrality of an atom is maintained by the balance of positively-charged protons with negatively-charged electrons. Protons and neutrons, in turn, are composed of still smaller particles whose properties are the subject of intensive research in physics.

The electron is exceedingly light when compared with either a neutron or a proton. In fact, the mass of either a proton or a neutron is about 1845 times as great as that of an electron.

While an atom in itself is exceedingly small, the exterior dimensions of an atom are much greater than the particles that make up the atom. The diameter of an atom is about 10^{-8} centimeter, whereas the diameter of its nucleus is on the order of 10^{-12} to 10^{-13} centimeter. The dimensions of electrons are poorly known, but they are smaller still. Because the space occupied by the nucleus and the electrons is much less than the atom as a whole, the proportion of an atom's volume occupied by matter is exceedingly small, being on the order of 10^{-12} of its total volume. Thus, most of an atom is empty space.

Because the protons in the nucleus of an atom all possess the same positive charge, and since like charges tend to repel each other, the nucleus of an atom would tend to fly apart if it were not for some binding force that holds the nucleus together. This binding force, whatever its nature, is relatively great, causing particles in the nucleus to be very closely held together. In fact, the particles are so close that the density of the nucleus is about 2×10^{14} grams per cubic centimeter.

There are, of course, different kinds of atoms or nuclides. There are more than 92 known naturally occurring chemical elements and a number of artificially prepared heavy elements. In addition, most elements consist of more than one nuclide, reflecting differences in the constitution of their nuclei. The difference between an atom of one element and an atom of another element is related to the number of protons in the atom's nucleus, which for a given atom is also the same as the number of orbital electrons. This number is termed the *atomic number*. Another important number is its *mass number*. Almost all of the mass of an atom is in its nucleus, and is due to the aggregation of protons and neutrons. The mass number is the sum of the number of protons and number of neutrons. The number of neutrons in atoms of a given element can vary. Oxygen, for example, has 8 protons, but different oxygen atoms have either 8, 9, or 10 neutrons. The mass numbers of oxygen are either 16, 17, or 18. These different nuclides of oxygen are its *isotopes* and may be identified by the mass number as a suffix, as for example, oxygen-16, oxygen-17 and oxygen-18. If you wish to determine the number of neutrons of a nuclide, merely subtract its atomic number from its mass number.

NATURE OF RADIOACTIVITY

In 1895, Roentgen, a German physicist, discovered X-rays. He noted that X-rays possess the ability to cause glass walls of tubes in which they were generated to fluoresce. Following his discovery, other physicists sought natural substances that might emit natural radiation with the properties of X-rays. In 1896, Becquerel, a French physicist, noted that photographic plates that had not been exposed to the light were darkened when placed near uranium compounds. These observations marked the discovery of radioactivity. Pierre Curie, the French physicist, and his Polish-born wife, Marie Curie, concluded in 1898 that the rays emitted by uranium are a fundamental property of the element uranium and are not related to the manner in which the uranium is chemically combined. Madam Curie, in 1898, discovered that the element thorium also emits radiation.

The binding forces that hold the protons and neutrons together in the nucleus of an atom act at exceeding short distances. When the nucleus disintegrates, the particles in it fly out at very high velocity.

Atoms can be split or caused to disintegrate artificially by bombardment with neutrons. On the other hand, in the isotopes of some elements, there are too many protons and neutrons packed in the nucleus to be held together indefinitely by the binding forces. These particles in the nucleus vibrate constantly and occasionally the binding forces are exceeded and part of the nucleus flies off naturally and spontaneously. This is *radioactivity*.

The nuclei of atoms break down in different ways. One way is by loss of a fragment consisting of two neutrons and two protons. This fragment is the nucleus of the helium atom, is termed an *alpha particle*, and has a mass of four. Thus, when an alpha particle is given off, the atom that sheds it acquires a new mass number that is necessarily four less than before. Also, since the alpha particle contains two protons, it also requires that the atomic number decline by two because it contains two less protons. Thus, loss of an alpha particle results in transformation of one element into another.

When an alpha particle is given off, it commonly leaves the nucleus of the atom in an *excited state*. The nucleus does not remain in this state, but eventually settles down to its normal stable state. In order to settle down, however, it must lose some of its energy. It does this by emitting one or more gamma rays, which are akin to other electromagnetic radiation which includes visible light, radiant heat, radio waves, and X-rays.

A second way in which radioactive decay may occur is by ejection of a *beta particle* from the nucleus of the atom. A beta particle is a fast-moving electron derived from a neutron. Since an electron possesses a single negative charge, its loss causes the neutron to lose its electrical neutrality and it is left with a positive charge. In other words, it has been changed into a proton. When a beta particle is emitted, the atom is transformed into the chemical element whose atomic number is one greater than before, since the number of protons has increased by one. A beta particle or electron, however, has almost negligible mass and loss of a beta particle does not result in change of mass number. In addition a small particle, termed a *neutrino*, is also given off when a beta particle is emitted.

The processes of radioactive decay illustrate the equivalence of mass and energy. When an alpha particle is given off, the mass of the alpha particle plus the mass of the nucleus that remains is slightly less than the mass of the orginal nucleus. The loss in mass is the mass-equivalent of energy created in the process of decay. The "lost" mass has been literally transformed into energy. This newly-formed energy is represented by kinetic energy of the alpha particle shot out and the kinetic energy of the atom that shed it, which recoils in the opposite direction. The increase in energy and the lost mass are related by the familiar Einstein equation, $E=mc^2$, where E is the energy resulting from decay, m is the lost mass, and c is the velocity of light, equal to 186,000 miles per second, or about 3×10^{10} centimeters per second.

When a beta particle is emitted, the energy of the beta particle plus gamma radiation is not enough, in terms of mass-equivalence, to equal the difference in mass before and after the beta particle is emitted. It was theorized that part of this mass difference is due to emission of another particle of very small mass, termed a *neutrino* because it does not possess an electric charge. The neutrino was detected experimentally some years after its existence had been postulated.

A third type of radioactive transformation is termed *electron capture*. When electron capture takes place, the nucleus of an atom captures an electron from its innermost orbital shell (K-shell). When this happens, one of the protons in the nucleus acquires the electron and is transformed into a neutron. The result is that the number of protons (atomic number) decreases by one, and the number of neutrons increases by one. The mass number, however, stays the same. Emission of a neutrino and a gamma ray accompany the transformation.

Some radioactive nuclides may decay in two or more possible ways, termed branching decay. At a particular step in a branching decay process, two alternate routes exist. For example potassium-40 may decay either by emission of a beta particle to produce calcium-40, or by electron capture to produce argon-40 (Figure 53). The "choice" of one of two alternative paths is statistical; the route of an individual atom can be predicted only as a matter of probability.

Part of the energy released by radioactive decay, as we have seen, is initially manifested in the increase of kinetic energy, represented by

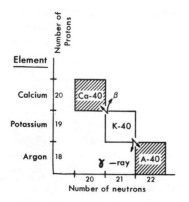

Figure 53. Decay routes of potassium-40. About 88% of potassium-40 atoms decay by emission of a beta particle to produce calcium-40. The remainder undergo electron capture (emitting gamma rays) to produce argon-40.

the velocities imparted to the emitted particles and the recoiling parent nuclei. This increase in kinetic energy is eventually transferred to other particles and appears as heat. Because radioactive nuclides are widespread, radioactive decay is an important source of heat within the earth. The structure and history of the earth undoubtedly would have been vastly different if there were no radioactive materials within it.

PROBABILITY AND RADIOACTIVITY

Radioactivity may be viewed in terms of probability. Radioactivity may be considered to be the probability that a given nuclide will be transformed spontaneously into another nuclide. If this probability is zero or very small, the nuclide is stable or only weakly radioactive. If it is great, the nuclide is strongly radioactive. Radioactivity is an attempt of a nuclide to achieve a more stable configuration of the particles within its nucleus. Some nuclides must undergo more than one consecutive change before stability is reached, thus forming a radioactive chain, or series.

Since radioactive transformation, or decay, is a matter of probability, it must be treated statistically. If one considers a single atom of a radioactive nuclide, it is impossible to predict when it will decay. It might decay in the next millionth of a second, or it might be unchanged a billion years from now. One can only express the probability that this individual atom will decay within a certain span of time. By considering large numbers of atoms, however, and measuring the average rate at which they decay, it is possible to predict the proportion that will have decayed within a given span of time.

The number of atoms of a nuclide that decay in an interval of time is proportional to the total number of atoms of the parent nuclide present. Because the disintegration is a continuous process, considering large numbers of atoms, the number of atoms that have not yet decayed will become smaller and smaller, while the number of atoms of the daughter nuclide will become larger and larger, provided that the daughter product is not, also, radioactive. Since the number of atoms decaying in unit time is proportional to the total number present, a constant, termed the *decay constant*, expresses this proportionality. Each radioactive nuclide has a characteristic decay constant. The decay constant is virtually unaffected by most known chemical or physical processes, and it seems certain that decay constants of the various radioactive nuclides have remained the same throughout geologic time.

Because radioactive decay is a random or chance process, the decay constant may be regarded as a measure of the probability that an atom will decay in a given span of time. Fluctuations occur in the number of atoms that disintegrate in a specimen during a small span of time, as for example, a few seconds or minutes. If the number of disintegrating atoms is small, these fluctuations will be greater than if the number of disintegrating atoms were large.

Because the decay of individual radioactive atoms is at random, it will take an extremely long time for all radioactive atoms of a given sample to be completely transformed into the decay product. Theoretically, it will take an infinite amount of time for all atoms to decay. But, because the atoms of a given radioactive nuclide decay at a certain average rate, it will require a finite amount of time for a fraction of the atoms initially present to decay. It is convenient to consider the time required for half of the atoms to decay. This time is said to be the *half-life* of the nuclide. When a period of time equal to the half-life has elapsed, half of the number of atoms originally present in any specified quantity (assuming the quantity contains many atoms) will have decayed. At the end of a period equal to twice the half-life, half of a half, or one-fourth, the original number of atoms will be left, and so on. Thus, the proportion of the original number of atoms that remain may be calculated if the amount of time that has passed is known. The half-life and the decay constant are closely related, both being measures of rate of decay.

Each radioactive nuclide has a particular half-life. The half-lives of radioactive species differ enormously, ranging from less than a billionth of a second to many billion years. In fact the half-lives of the stable nuclides may be considered to be infinite, since there is no sharp division between stable nuclides and those with finite but extremely long half-lives.

It is convenient to express radioactive decay graphically. Figure 54 shows the relationship between the proportion of radioactive parent remaining and elapsed time measured in half-lives. The graph is valid for any radioactive nuclide, regardless of the length of its half-life. If the proportion of radioactive parent remaining is shown on a logarithmic scale instead of a linear scale, a straight line relates the proportion remaining to time in half-lives (Figure 55).

MATHEMATICAL STATEMENT OF LAW OF GROWTH AND DECAY

The fundamental law of radioactive decay states that the number of atoms decaying in a unit amount of time, $-dN/dt$, is proportional to the number of atoms present, N. This may be stated in the differential equation

$$\frac{-dN}{dt} = \lambda N \tag{1}$$

where t = time,
λ = decay constant, and
N = number of atoms present.

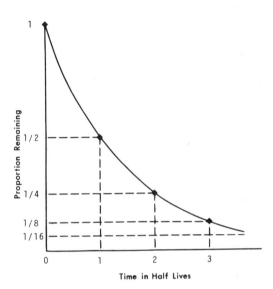

Figure 54. Graph illustrating law of radioactive decay with proportion of radioactive parent remaining drawn on a linear scale.

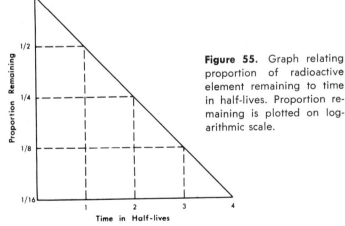

Figure 55. Graph relating proportion of radioactive element remaining to time in half-lives. Proportion remaining is plotted on logarithmic scale.

The negative sign is employed because the number of atoms becomes less with time. If this equation is integrated and rearranged we obtain

$$N = N_o e^{-\lambda t} \tag{2}$$

where N_0 = number of atoms present at time t = 0,
    e = base of natural logarithms, and
    N = number of atoms present now.

The decay constant and the half-life of a radioactive nuclide are related. This may be expressed by rearranging the above equation, so that

$$\frac{N}{N_0} = e^{-\lambda t} \tag{3}$$

If 1/2 is substituted for N/N_0 and T for time equal to one half-life, then the equation may be rewritten as

$$1/2 = e^{-\lambda T} \tag{4}$$

This equation may be rewritten in turn as

$$\log_e 1/2 = -\lambda T \tag{5}$$

where $\log_e$ indicates the natural logarithm.
Rearranging again,

$$-0.69315 = -\lambda T \tag{6}$$

or

$$T = \frac{0.69315}{\lambda} \tag{7}$$

Stated in words the half-life, T, of any radioactive nuclide is equal to 0.69315 divided by its decay constant.

Relation Between Parent and Daughter Nuclides

When an atom of a radioactive nuclide decays, an atom of a daughter nuclide is formed. The daughter nuclide may be stable, and no further decay is possible, or it may be unstable and decay in turn. If unstable, and depending on the particular radioactive nuclide being considered, the decay rate of the daughter may be faster or slower than that of the parent. If a rock or mineral contains both a decaying parent and daughter, the proportion of the two depend on whether the parent or daughter has the longest half-life. If the parent is shorter-lived than the daughter and if the rock or mineral was originally free of the daughter, then the amount of the daughter will increase to a maximum and then decrease. The proportion of parent to daughter will not be constant, regardless of the amount of time that elapses.

If the parent decays more slowly than the daughter, a steady state, termed *radioactive equilibrium*, will eventually be reached. A steady state is attained when the number of daughter atoms that decay per unit time is equal to the number of daughter atoms formed through decay of the parent. At that point, the ratio of number of atoms of parent and daughter is a constant, the ratio being a function of the decay constants of parent and daughter, as indicated by the equation

$$\frac{N_1}{N_2} = \frac{\lambda_2 - \lambda_1}{\lambda_1} \tag{8}$$

where N_1 = number of atoms of parent,
$\quad\quad N_2$ = number of atoms of daughter,
$\quad\quad \lambda_1$ = decay constant of parent, and
$\quad\quad \lambda_2$ = decay constant of daughter.

If the parent is much longer lived than the daughter, so that decrease in the amount of parent is small during several half-lives of the daughter, the decay constant of the parent is necessarily much less than that of the daughter. In this case, the above equation is simplified to

$$\frac{N_1}{N_2} = \frac{\lambda_2}{\lambda_1} \tag{9}$$

which, upon rearranging, gives

$$N_1\lambda_1 = N_2\lambda_2 \tag{10}$$

Since the decay rate, or number of disintegrations per unit time is given by the equation

$$-\frac{dN}{dt} = \lambda N \tag{11}$$

it may be seen that equation 11 expresses both the rate of decay of parent and production of daughter, which are equal when a steady state has been attained.

Because the half-life (T) of a radioactive nuclide is related to its decay constant by the equation

$$\lambda = \frac{0.69315}{T} \tag{12}$$

we may substitute T for λ in Equation 10, which yields

$$\frac{0.69315}{T_1}N_1 = \frac{0.69315}{T_2}N_2 \tag{13}$$

The constant 0.69315 may be dropped, simplifying the equation to

$$\frac{N_1}{T_1} = \frac{N_2}{T_2} \tag{14}$$

or

$$\frac{N_1}{N_2} = \frac{T_1}{T_2} \tag{15}$$

Stated in words, when the parent decays more slowly than the daughter, and when radioactive equilibrium has been attained, the ratio of numbers of parent and daughter atoms is proportional to the ratio of the half-lives of parent and daughter.

RADIOACTIVE NUCLIDES

There are a large number of nuclides that undergo radioactive decay. Many nuclides with very short half-lives have been produced artificially. Radioactive nuclides that occur naturally on earth may be divided into two general classes, (1) those that are continually being produced by neutron bombardment and which have relatively short half-lives (Table 7) and (2) those that were inherited when the earth was formed and have long half-lives (Table 8). In turn, the long-lived nuclides may be divided into two subclasses: (a) those with atomic numbers of 82 or less that undergo decay in a single step; and those of atomic numbers of 83 to 92 which are members of three radioactive series in which there are multiple steps in the decay process.

TABLE 7

Neutron-induced radioactive nuclides.

Nuclide	Half-life
Hydrogen-3	12.3 years
Beryllium-10	2.7 million years
Carbon-14	5730 years
Sodium-22	2.6 years
Aluminum-26	0.74 million years
Silicon-32	700 years
Chlorine-36	0.31 million years
Argon-39	260 years

Radioactive Series

With exception of artificially produced nuclides, and lead-204 and bismuth-209, which occur naturally, most nuclides of atomic number 82 and higher are members of three radioactive series, the uranium-238 series, the uranium-235 series, and the thorium-232 series. The decay curves of these series are shown in Figure 56. These three radioactive series exist on the earth today by virtue of the fact that the parent nuclide of each series is long lived. Uranium-238 (parent of the uranium-

TABLE 8

Long-lived radioactive nuclides.

	Parent	Daughter	Half-life in years	Type of Decay
	Potassium-40	Argon-40	1.3×10^9	Electron capture
		Calcium-40		Beta
s	Vanadium-50	Titanium-50	6×10^{15}	Electron capture
i		Chromium-50		Beta
n	Rubidium-87	Strontium-87	4.7×10^{10}	Beta
g	Indium-115	Tin-155	5×10^{14}	Beta
l	Tellurium-123	Antimony-123	1.2×10^{13}	Electron capture
e	Lanthanum-138	Barium-138	1.1×10^{11}	Electron capture
		Cerium-138		Beta
s	Cerium-142	Barium-138	5×10^{15}	Alpha
t	Neodymium-144	Cerium-140	2.4×10^{15}	Alpha
e	Samarium-147	Neodymium-143	1.06×10^{11}	Alpha
p	Samarium-148	Neodymium-144	1.2×10^{13}	Alpha
	Samarium-149	Neodymium-145	4×10^{14}	Alpha
d	Gadolinium-152	Samarium-148	1.1×10^{14}	Alpha
e	Dysprosium-156	Gadolinium-152	2×10^{14}	Alpha
c	Hafnium-174	Ytterbium-170	4.3×10^{15}	Alpha
a	Lutetium-176	Hafnium-176	2.2×10^{10}	Beta
y	Rhenium-187	Osmium-187	4×10^{10}	Beta
	Platinum-190	Osmium-186	7×10^{11}	Alpha
	Lead-204	Mercury-200	1.4×10^{17}	Alpha
s d	Thorium-232	Lead-208	1.41×10^{10}	6 alpha + 4 beta
e e				
r c	Uranium-235	Lead-207	7.13×10^{8}	7 alpha + 4 beta
i a				
e y	Uranium-238	Lead-206	4.51×10^{9}	8 alpha + 6 beta
s				

238 series) has a half-life of about 4.5 billion years, thorium-232 has a half-life of about 14.1 billion years and uranium-235 has a half-life of about 713 million years.

There is a fourth radioactive series, sometimes termed the neptunium series, that is composed of nuclides with relatively short half-lives except for long-lived bismuth-209 and the final stable end product, thallium-205. Virtually, all of the short-lived nuclides, which are higher in the series than bismuth-209, must have decayed early in the earth's history. Consequently, the neptunium series is of no direct value for age-dating purposes.

The uranium-238 series possesses a total of nineteen members. Beginning with the parent uranium-238, a series of successive transformations takes place, in which alpha and beta particles are emitted. The succession of transformations is illustrated in Figure 57, which is a graph

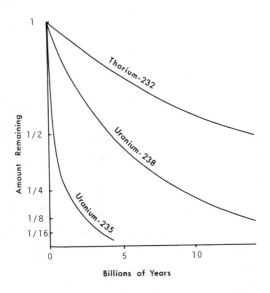

Figure 56. Decay curves for uranium-235, uranium-238, and thorium-232.

in which each member of the uranium-238 series is plotted according to its number of protons and number of neutrons. The type of particle emitted during each transformation is shown. The end product in the series is lead-206, which is stable and cannot undergo further decay.

There are alternative or branching decay routes in the lower part of the uranium-238 series, decay occurring by either emission of a beta particle or by an alpha particle. The route taken by an individual atom at each branch point can only be predicted statistically. For example, an atom of polonium-218 may decay either by loss of a beta particle or loss of an alpha particle. If a beta particle is given off, a neutron is transformed into a proton, and astatine-218 is produced. Astatine has one more proton and one less neutron than polonium-218, but has the same mass number as polonium-218 because the loss of a beta particle results in only an extremely small loss in mass. On the other hand, if an alpha particle is given off, lead-214 is produced, containing two neutrons and two protons less than polonium-218. Figure 58 lists the nuclides of the uranium-238 family, their half-lives, and the percentages of atoms that follow alternative routes at branch points.

It should also be emphasized that any given atom of uranium-238 that is eventually transformed to lead-206, goes through fourteen suc-

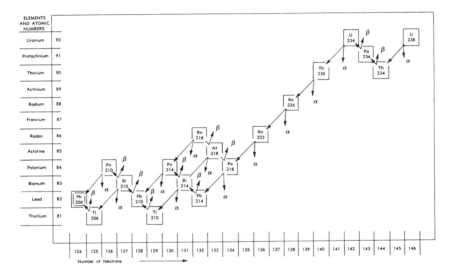

Figure 57. Diagram showing radioactive transformations in uranium-238 series. Twelve element names and their atomic numbers are shown on vertical scale; number of neutrons is shown on horizontal scale. Curving arrows denote ejection of particle (alpha particle or beta particle) from nucleus.

cessive decay steps and represents, in succession, a total of fifteen of the nuclides of the uranium-238 series. Since there are nineteen nuclides of the uranium-238, the difference between nineteen and fifteen is due to the presence of alternative decay routes, which permit a given atom to represent only fifteen of the nuclides as it is successively transformed.

The thorium-232 series (Figure 59) possesses a total of thirteen nuclides which are represented in the decay of thorium-232 to lead-208. In the transformation to the stable end product, lead-208, any given atom of thorium-232 undergoes ten decay steps and represents eleven of the thirteen nuclides because alternative decay routes exist. As in the uranium-238 series, individual decay steps consist of either emission of an alpha particle or a beta particle.

DECAY CLOCKS

Radiometric age dating methods may be divided into two general classes (1) *decay clocks* that depend on radioactive decay of naturally occurring short-lived nuclides that are currently being produced by either neutron bombardment, or by radioactive decay within the uranium and thorium series, and (2) *accumulation clocks* which depend on long-

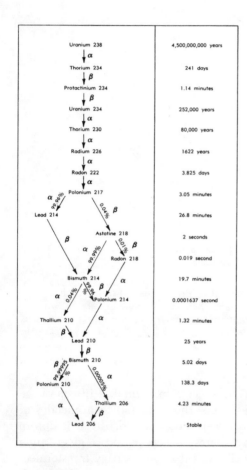

Figure 58. Diagram showing decay routes of uranium-238 series and half-lives of members of series.

lived radioactive nuclides inherited when the earth was formed. Accumulation clocks are based on the proportion of a radioactive parent that decays to an accumulating daughter nuclide. Thus, there are important differences in analytical methods pertaining to the two types of clocks; the proportion of daughter product formed is not necessarily considered in a decay clock, but must be measured in an accumulation clock.

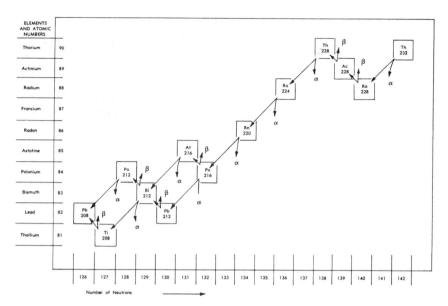

Figure 59. Diagram showing radioactive transformations in thorium-232 series.

When a radioactive nuclide is produced by a nuclear reaction, such as neutron bombardment, the proportion of the radioactive nuclide gradually reaches a constant value as an equilibrium condition is reached in the system being considered. If a part of this system is then isolated so that no more of the radioactive nuclide is added, the radioactive material that remains in the isolated part will continue to decay at a rate specified by its decay constant or half-life. Thus, a decay clock provides a measure of age because the proportion of radioactive nuclide that remains is a function of the time that has elapsed since the material analyzed was isolated from the system in which the radioactive nuclide was produced.

Both types of clocks have limits. Since the proportion of radioactive parent remaining declines steadily, the reliability of age calculations tends to decrease as age increases. The limit is not more than about 10 half-lives, at which point the proportion of radioactive parent has declined to about 1/1000 of that originally present.

Carbon-14 Decay Clock

The carbon-14 decay clock is widely used for determining the ages of materials that contain carbon and that are less than about 40,000 or 50,000 years old. Carbon-14 is produced when a nitrogen-14 nucleus absorbs a neutron, and in turn emits a proton. Carbon-14, which has a half-life of 5730 years, decays by emission of a beta particle, reverting back to nitrogen-14. Carbon-14 is produced in the atmosphere above an altitude of 30,000 feet. Here cosmic rays consisting mostly of protons traveling at very high velocities enter the atmosphere and collide with the nuclei of atoms composing the atmospheric gases. The collisions produce nuclear debris that includes neutrons. The neutrons in turn react with nitrogen-14 and other atomic nuclei.

Newly created carbon-14 continually enters the world reservoir of carbon. The carbon-14 atoms combine with oxygen to produce carbon dioxide. Some of this carbon dioxide containing carbon-14 remains in the air, while some enters into solution in the oceans, from which it is subsequently partly removed through precipitation of calcium carbonate and by photosynthesis of marine algae. Much of the carbon dioxide in the air is removed by land plants through photosynthesis, and in turn, incorporated in animals via the food chain. Thus, carbon-14 is present in all living material and forms a major source of radiation affecting organisms. For example, on the order of 200,000 carbon-14 atoms decay each minute in a man's body. Most carbon-14 age determinations are based on analysis of former living material of either plant or animal origin.

Carbon-14 dating is accomplished by counting the atomic disintegrations that occur within a sample in a given amount of time, employing sensitive counting devices that are shielded to reduce the effects of cosmic radiation and other background radiation.

The carbon-14 age-dating method is based on removal of material containing carbon-14 from the world exchange reservoir of carbon. The carbon-14 method is based on the assumption that the time required for mixing in the reservoir is relatively short compared with the subsequent elapsed time which is to be measured. Thus if 200 years were required for growth of a tree that yielded wood specimens which are now 10,000 years old, the 200 years during which the tree reacted with the atmosphere is short compared with the present age of the wood.

The validity of the carbon-14 has been tested on materials whose age is known by tree-ring dating or from human history. Table 9 shows expected ages and carbon-14 ages of three specimens of wood. The carbon-14 ages do not correspond perfectly with expected ages, each being accompanied by a range of error, but the accordance is relatively good.

Carbon-14 dating has had great influence in geology and archeology. Advances and retreats of glaciers that have occurred within the last 35,000 to 40,000 years may be dated by the carbon-14 method. Appli-

TABLE 9

Comparison of expected ages of three wood specimens
with their carbon-14 ages.

	Expected Age	Carbon-14 Age
Tree Ring, Douglas Fir New Mexico	1, 372 yrs.	1, 050 yrs.
Coffin wood, Egypt	2, 280 yrs.	2, 200 yrs.
Acacia wood, Tomb of Zoser, Sakkara, Egypt	4, 650 yrs.	4, 000 yrs.

cations to archeology have been particularly spectacular. For example, carbon-14 dates suggest that man first appeared in North America about 11,000 years ago, substantially later than thought previously.

ACCUMULATION CLOCKS

Accumulation clocks are based on the accumulation of a daughter nuclide produced by decay of its radioactive parent. In a closed system, the amount of parent continually decreases and the amount of daughter continually increases. Application of an accumulation clock method requires several assumptions: (1) The decay constant or half-life must be accurately known; (2) the sample analyzed must be representative of the geologic body to be dated; (3) the final daughter product, and intermediate decay products transitional between the parent and the final daughter product must not have been present in the sample when it was formed or if they were, they must be considered in making calculations; (4) there must have been no gain or loss in either the parent or the daughter product in the sample after it formed due to solution or diffusion. If these assumptions are satisfied, the age of a sample containing a radioactive nuclide is a function of the proportion of parent and daughter nuclides.

Most applications of accumulation clock methods depend upon crystals that have served as tight, closed systems for long intervals of time. In many examples, crystals do appear to have sheltered both parent and daughter nuclides from losses or gains from outside. On the other hand, losses or gains due to solution and diffusion must always be suspected, for some crystals have yielded very erroneous age dates because of the effects of solution and diffusion.

Fundamental Age Equations

Let us reconsider the equation that describes the decay of a radioactive parent to a daughter product. This equation states that the number of atoms decaying in a unit amount of time is proportional to the number of atoms present, and may be written

$$- \frac{dN}{dt} = \lambda N \tag{16}$$

where t = interval of time,

λ = decay constant, and

N = number of atoms present.

If we assume a simplified situation, namely that the parent radioactive isotope decays directly to a single stable isotope, we may adopt the above equation to express the relation between the amount of the parent that existed initially and the amount that exists at present, after an interval of time has passed. This equation may be written

$$- \frac{dP}{dt} = \lambda P \tag{17}$$

Upon integration

$$P_i = P_p \, e^{\lambda t} \tag{18}$$

where P_i = the number of atoms of parent initially existing,

P_p = number of atoms of parent existing at present,

t = interval of time separating P_i and P_p,

e = base of natural logarithms, and

λ = decay constant.

Now let us carry the analysis a step further. Since we have assumed that the parent decays to the daughter directly, there is a simple relation between the difference between the amount of parent initially existing and that existing at present, and the difference between the amount of daughter initially existing and the amount of daughter at present. This relation may be expressed with an equation as

$$D_p - D_i = P_i - P_p \tag{19}$$

where D_i = number of atoms of daughter existing initially, and

D_p = number of atoms of daughter existing at present.

This equation states that the number of atoms of parent that decay in an interval of time will be exactly equal to the number of daughter atoms produced. In other words, this equation states that the difference between the number of daughter atoms at present existing in the system (D_p) and the number of daughter atoms existing initially in the system (D_i) will be equal to the difference between the number of parent atoms existing initially (P_i) and the number of parent atoms at present

(P_p). The number of daughter atoms is constantly growing larger while the number of parent atoms is growing smaller, accounting for the positive and negative signs used in the equation.

We may modify Equation 19 above by substituting for P_i from Equation 18.

$$D_p - D_i = P_p e^{\lambda t} - P_p \qquad (20)$$

This equation may be rewritten in turn

$$D_p - D_i = P_p(e^{\lambda t} - 1) \qquad (21)$$

Rearranging to solve for t, we obtain, in succession:

$$\frac{D_p - D_i}{P_p} = e^{\lambda t} - 1 \qquad (22)$$

$$e^{\lambda t} = \frac{D_p - D_i}{P_p} + 1 \qquad (23)$$

$$\lambda t = \log_e\left[\frac{D_p - D_i}{P_p} + 1\right] \qquad (24)$$

$$t = \frac{1}{\lambda} \log_e\left[\frac{D_p - D_i}{P_p} + 1\right] \qquad (25)$$

Equation 25 represents an adaptation of the fundamental equation for calculating age. Since we may determine the amount of daughter (D_p) and parent (P_p) existing at present by analysis, and since the decay constant (λ) is known, we may calculate time (t) if the amount of daughter (D_i) initially existing is known.

Uranium-lead and Thorium-lead Methods

The uranium-lead and thorium-lead methods are based on the decay of uranium and thorium to produce the three stable isotopes of lead. Lead-206 is the final daughter product of uranium-238, lead-207 of uranium-235, and lead-208 of thorium-232. As a result, the amounts of these three lead isotopes are constantly increasing on the earth. A fourth naturally occurring isotope of lead exists, lead-204. Lead-204, although not produced by radioactive decay, is weakly radioactive, decaying extremely slowly to mercury-200 (Table 8). The relative proportions of the four lead isotopes in the earth's crust are listed in Table 10.

Determination of geologic age of uranium or thorium-bearing minerals is carried out by analyzing the mineral for amounts of the two uranium isotopes, for thorium, and for the four lead isotopes. Inasmuch as uranium-235 and uranium-238 tend to occur in constant proportions with respect to each other, a single determination of uranium suffices. Relative amounts of the four isotopes of lead may be determined with a mass spectrometer, an analytical instrument capable of separating and measuring the proportions of minute particles according to their mass

TABLE 10

Approximate relative proportions of lead isotopes in earth's crust.

Lead-204	1.5%
Lead-206	25.5%
Lead-207	21%
Lead-208	52%

differences. Each lead isotope may be distinguished from other lead isotopes by its mass.

Minerals that contain uranium may also contain thorium. In many cases, the presence of two uranium isotopes, plus thorium, permits three separate determinations to be made. Calculation of ages may be according to formulas, or in principle, they may be carried out by reference to graphs. Graphs pertaining to the uranium-238/lead-206 method are shown in Figures 60 and 61. Figure 60 contains three curves: One shows the weight proportion of uranium that remains, versus elapsed time,

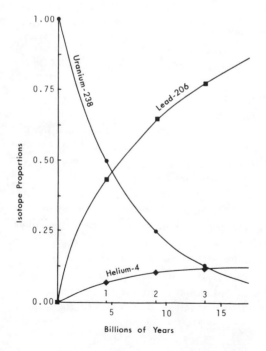

Figure 60. Graph showing weight proportions of uranium-238, lead-206 and helium-4 with respect to time. Half-lives of uranium-238 are also shown on horizontal scale.

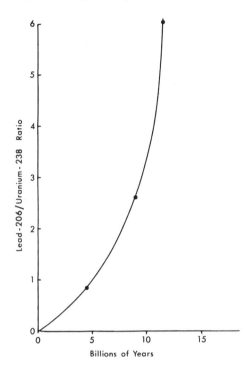

Figure 61. Graph showing ratio of lead-206/uranium-238 with respect to time.

beginning with a unit amount of uranium; the other two show the proportions of lead-206 and helium-4 produced. When an atom of uranium-238 decays, it yields an atom of lead-206 and eight alpha particles (Figure 57). An alpha particle is a helium-4 nucleus. These transformations may be written

$$U^{238} \longrightarrow Pb^{206} + 8He^4$$

where U^{238} = uranium-238,
$\quad Pb^{206}$ = lead-206, and
$\quad He^4$ = helium-4.

The mass of parent atom, and the sum of the masses of the daughter atoms are identical:

$$238 = 206 + 32.$$

Thus, when any specified amount of uranium-238 decays, the weight proportion of lead produced is

$$\frac{206}{238} = 0.866$$

and the weight proportion of helium produced is

$$\frac{32}{238} = 0.134.$$

These ratios are usĕd in calculating the points graphed in Figure 60. For example, when one half-life has elapsed, 0.5 of a unit amount of uranium has decayed to yield 0.866 x 0.5 = 0.433 units of lead. Calculations for other points are similar. Although the curves shown in Figure 60 illustrate the changes in proportions of uranium, lead, and helium with time, they do not show, directly, the changes in proportion of uranium and lead with respect to each other. A more useful graph, which can be used with analytical data, is shown in Figure 61, where variations in the lead-206/uranium-238 ratio with respect to time are plotted. The points shown in this curve are calculated in a simple manner, illustrated in Table 11. To use this graph for an age determination, simply calculate the lead-206/uranium-238 ratio by dividing the amount of lead-206 by the amount of uranium-238, by weight, and refer to the graph. Curves for calculation of ages with the uranium-235/lead-207 method and the thorium-232/lead-208 method may be prepared in an analogous manner.

TABLE 11

Proportion of lead-206 and uranium-238, and ratio of
lead-206/uranium-238 with respect to elapsed time in half-lives.

	0	1	2	3	4
Lead-206	0.00	0.433	0.650	0.758	0.821
Uranium-238	1.00	0.500	0.250	0.125	0.062
Lead-206/Uranium-238	0.00	0.866	2.600	6.062	13.128

Correcting for Common Lead

The uranium-lead methods and the thorium-lead method for determining ages are accurate, without corrections, only if there has been no contamination by lead from other sources, or in other words, no lead is present that has not been produced by radioactive decay within the mineral analyzed. A uranium mineral analyzed with a mass spectrometer will be found to contain lead-206 and lead-207, and if thorium is present, lead-208 also will be found. These lead isotopes, at least in part, have been produced by radioactive decay of radioactive materials within the specimen. The question arises, however, as to whether any of the lead present in the specimen has not been produced by radioactive decay within the specimen. An answer may be obtained by analyzing the specimen for lead-204. If lead-204 is present, some of the lead has not been produced by radioactive decay, and therefore, suitable corrections must be made before age calculations are made.

Many minerals, including galena, contain lead that is not associated with significant amounts of uranium or thorium. This lead is termed "common" lead, and is distinguished from lead produced solely through decay of uranium and thorium by the presence of lead-204. Common lead also contains the other three lead isotopes, although it contains a higher proportion of lead-207 than lead produced through radioactive decay (radiogenic lead).

Because lead-204 is not produced through radioactive decay, the presence of lead-204 in a uranium or thorium-bearing mineral is a guide to the proportion of common lead incorporated in the mineral. The common lead may have been incorporated in the mineral when it was initially formed, or it may have been added later by precipitation from solution. The central problem in correcting for the presence of common lead is to determine the proportions of lead-206, lead-207 and lead-208, with respect to lead-204, that are associated with the common lead present.

The isotopic composition of common lead has very gradually changed with time. The reason for this is that part of the common lead present in the earth (excluding lead-204) has been produced by radioactive decay. When the earth was first formed, it must have inherited certain amounts of all four lead isotopes. In addition, it inherited certain amounts of thorium and uranium. As the earth was differentiated into a core, mantle, and crust, some of the lead, uranium and thorium was disseminated in the outer part of the crust. This primeval material is the ultimate source of the uranium, thorium and lead present in rocks that we may analyze today. The proportions of different lead isotopes with respect to each other have been slowly changing with time in the crust. Perhaps two-thirds of the lead in the crust is primeval lead, whereas the other one-third is radiogenic lead produced by decay of uranium and thorium during the earth's estimated lifetime of about five billion years. The continual addition of radiogenic lead during this time is responsible for progressive change in the isotopic composition of common lead.

Here we have a paradox. Even part of the common lead has an ultimate radioactive origin. As uranium and thorium in the crust have decayed, they have yielded lead-206, 207 and 208. But, chemical processes of solution and precipitation have tended to separate the lead isotopes thus produced from their parent uranium and thorium. In turn, these radiogenic lead isotopes have been progressively added to the primeval lead, causing the stock of common lead in the crust to grow larger and larger, and slowly altering its isotopic composition.

Thus, the lead isotope ratios in a specimen containing no lead other than common lead tend to reflect the isotopic composition of common lead formed at a particular time in the past. If additional radiogenic lead is not incorporated in the common lead, the isotopic composition will remain more or less unchanged. Figure 62 contains three curves which represent the changing proportions of lead-206, lead-207 and lead-208 with respect to lead-204 in common lead during the past 4½ billion years.

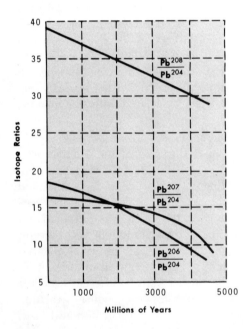

Figure 62. Graphs showing changes in isotope ratios in common lead in the earth during the past 4-½ billion years. Curves are based on mass spectrometric analysis of many samples. Individual data points are not shown here. Adapted from Russell and Farquhar (1960).

In making age determinations, it is necessary to subtract the common lead from the radiogenic lead. To do this one needs to know two things: The rough age of the mineral and proportion of lead-204. By referring to Figure 62, one can find the approximate ratios of lead-206, lead-207 and lead-208 to lead-204 for any given age. Then, if the amount of lead-204 present is known, the amounts of lead-206, lead-207 and lead-208 that are common lead will be proportional to the lead-204 according to the ratios given by the graph. The amounts of common lead can then be subtracted before more precise ages are calculated.

Concordant and Discordant Ages

One of the strengths of the uranium-lead and thorium-lead methods is that three to four independent age determinations may be obtained from a single specimen. If the ages are in relative agreement with each other, they are said to be *concordant*; if the calculated ages differ by 10 percent or more, they may be considered to be *discordant*. Naturally, there is no sharp boundary between concordant and discordant ages. In uranium-bearing specimens, it is possible to make two independent determinations of age employing the lead-206/uranium-238 ratio and the lead-207/uranium-235 ratio, particularly if the ages are greater than about 300 million years. In thorium-bearing specimens, the age is determined by the lead-208/thorium-232 ratio. In many specimens, both uranium and thorium are present, permitting three distinct age determinations to be made.

In addition to the use of the three ratios listed above, a useful measure of age is provided by the ratio of lead-207 with respect to lead-206. Because the half-life of uranium-235 (0.7 billion years) is much less than the half-life of uranium-238 (4.5 billion years), the amount of lead-207 produced by decay of uranium-235 within a mineral drops off much more rapidly than the amount of lead-238. Consequently, the ratio lead-207/lead-206, in itself, forms a good radioactive clock and is useful for dating specimens more than half a billion years old. Furthermore, the lead-207/lead-206 ratio is less likely to be affected by partial loss of lead due to solution, because even if lead is lost, the two leads behave similarly from a chemical point of view, their ratio being little changed. A graph of lead-207/lead-206 ratio, versus time, is shown in Figure 63. This graph pertains to lead produced by radioactive decay within the specimen. If ages of samples contaminated with common lead are to be calculated, the amounts of lead-207 and lead-206 that form part of the common lead can be subtracted before the radiogenic lead-207/lead-206 ratio is calculated.

Table 12 presents results of radiometric ages obtained by different methods at six localities. The degree of concordance between the ages obtained by the uranium-lead methods, the thorium-lead method, and the lead-207/lead-206 method shows considerable variation. In addition, potassium-argon ages (described subsequently) are available for mica specimens obtained at three of the localities, and exhibit varying degrees of concordance with the uranium-lead and thorium-lead ages. The failure of the calculated ages to agree more closely in some of the examples may be ascribed to various causes, including unaccounted losses or gains of parent or daughter products due to diffusion or solution, and, to a lesser extent, to analytical errors.

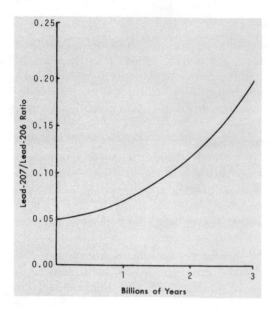

Figure 63. Graph of radiogenic lead-207/lead-206 ratio versus time.

TABLE 12

Degree of concordance between age estimates
determined by different methods.

Region	Mineral	Calculated Ages in Millions of Years				
		Lead-206 / Uranium-238	Lead-207 / Uranium-235	Lead-208 / Thorium-232	Lead-207 / Lead-206	Potassium-40 / Argon-40
(1) Union of South Africa	Zircon	330	354	237	525	
(2) Quebec	Thorianite Biotite	995	975	940	990	925
(3) South Dakota	Uraninite	1580	1600	1440	1630	
(4) Quebec	Uraninite Biotite	2000	1945	2120	1925	2015
(5) Southern Rhodesia	Monazite	2260	2470	2650		
(6) Southern Rhodesia	Monazite Mica	2675	2680	2645	2680	2310

The failure of any of the age values to exactly accord with each other emphasizes that each calculated age is accompanied by some degree of uncertainty. The calculated age values are not "absolute", but instead must be regarded as estimates of age accompanied by a margin of error.

POTASSIUM-ARGON AND RUBIDIUM-STRONTIUM METHODS

Potassium-argon Method

The potassium-argon method of age dating has certain advantages over the uranium and thorium-lead methods because potassium-bearing minerals are much more widespread than uranium-bearing minerals. Sedimentary rocks that contain glauconite, a potassium-bearing mineral, can be dated directly by potassium methods. Common igneous rocks also can be dated by the potassium-argon method. Biotite, which contains potassium, is a common mineral in granite and other igneous rocks and is well suited for potassium-argon analysis.

The element potassium consists of three isotopes, potassium-39, potassium-40 and potassium-41. Potassium-40 is radioactive, while the other two isotopes are stable. Potassium-40 decays via two alternate routes (Figure 53). About 88 percent of potassium-40 atoms decay via emission of a beta particle from a neutron, causing the neutron to become a proton and transforming the nucleus to calcium-40. The remaining 12 percent of potassium-40 atoms decay by electron capture, causing a proton to be transformed into a neutron and yielding argon-40 as a decay product.

In theory, ages could be determined by the potassium-40/calcium-40 ratio as well as the potassium-40/argon-40 ratio. Calcium-40, however, is so widespread that most specimens contain calcium-40 that has not been produced by radioactive decay within the specimen. Consequently, the potassium-calcium method has been employed very little. The potassium-argon method, however, avoids this difficulty and is widely used.

The first step in making a potassium-argon analysis is to separate the potassium-bearing mineral to be analyzed from the remainder of the rock. Mica, for example, can be separated from a granite following crushing and grinding. Argon-40 is determined by mass-spectrometric analysis of the argon released from the mineral. The argon is released by heating the mineral mixed with calcium chloride in a vacuum until it is molten and the entrapped gasses are given off. The potassium can be determined by flame photometric analysis of the powdered mineral, and the amount of potassium-40 calculated by multiplying the amount of total potassium present by 0.000119, because potassium-40 forms approximately 0.0119 percent of total potassium. Care must be taken to avoid contamination by argon present in the air, since about one percent of the air consists of argon-40. Fortunately, air argon always contains a small proportion of argon-36, permitting contamination to be detected. Given the proportions of argon-40 and potassium-40 present in the mineral, the age may be calculated by the use of an equation, or, in principle, by reference to graphs (Figures 64 and 65).

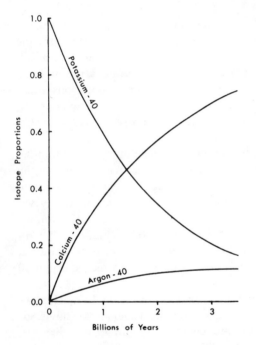

Figure 64. Graphs of variations in proportions of potassium-40, argon-40, and calcium-40 with time, beginning with a unit amount of potassium-40.

Reliable age determinations by the potassium-argon method require that argon-40, produced by the decay of potassium, not have leaked out of potassium-bearing crystals being dated. The common potassium micas, if well crystallized, appear to retain argon-40 if they have not been heated to above about 125 or 150°C. However, heating above this temperature range causes argon-40 to be lost. Consequently, ages of micas obtained by potassium-argon method tend to indicate the last period of heating rather than the time of origin. Glauconite, in sedimentary rocks, was orginally believed to retain most of the argon formed by decay of potassium-40. Now, however, it is known that glauconite does not behave as a closed system, tending to lose argon at relatively low temperatures. As a result, potassium-argon ages of sediments tend to be minimum age limits.

Rubidium-strontium Method

The rubidium-strontium method for dating is based on the decay of rubidium-87 to strontium-87. Although rubidium-87 is more abundant that potassium-40, the rate of decay of rubidium-87 is much slower (Table 8). The rubidium-strontium method does not depend on the presence of potassium, but rubidium tends to occur in minerals that are

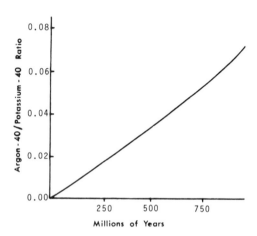

Figure 65. Graph of argon-40/potassium-40 ratio over one billion years. Curve is based on variations shown in Figure 64.

rich in potassium. As a result, it is commonly possible to compare ages obtained by both the rubidium-strontium and potassium-argon methods from the same mineral specimen. The mica minerals provide satisfactory samples for rubidium-strontium age determinations, as does orthoclase feldspar, which is common in many igneous rocks. Unfortunately, however, orthoclase generally does not yield valid potassium-argon dates for comparison purposes.

QUANTIFYING THE GEOLOGIC TIME SCALE

Construction of a quantitative scale of geologic time has been one of the foremost objectives of geology. Many quantitative age determinations are now available, but the basic difficulties of relating radiometric ages to a stratigraphic scale of time have not been completely resolved. An absolute scale of time must be built by interpolating between geologic events that can be dated in a quantitative scale of time, as well as accurately placed in the qualitative stratigraphic scale of time. Unfortunately, reliable "tie points" between the two scales are relatively rare.

Four general types of dated materials have been used as tie points in constructing an absolute scale of time: (1) layered volcanics, (2) bracketed intrusives, (3) simple intrusives and (4) glauconite present in sandstones and limestones.

Layered volcanics, consisting of lava flows and deposits of volcanic ash, provide the best tie points. Their excellence is due to the fact that they tend to have been deposited quickly and, in places, they occur interstratified within sequences of fossiliferous sedimentary rocks, permitting their postions to be more or less readily established in the stratigraphic scale of time. Furthermore, volcanics generally contain minerals that permit determination of ages by different methods. Zircon is present in some volcanics, permitting uranium-lead age determinations. Biotite is very common, permitting potassium-argon and rubidium-strontium age determinations. Consequently, multiple age determinations permit the degree of concordance to be ascertained. Fortunately, many of the layered volcanics that have been dated have yielded concordant ages, lending confidence to the validity of the calculated ages.

Bracketed intrusives (Figure 14) also provide valuable tie points. The stratigraphic age relationships of a bracketed intrusive, however, are necessarily less accurate than those associated with layered volcanics. The reason is that the relative age of the intrusive is bracketed between the age of the rock that is intruded, providing a maximum age, and the age of overlying strata, providing a minimum age. A bracketed intrusive is useful only if the span of time between the maximum and minimum ages is relatively small. Unfortunately, most bracketed intrusives are of little value for time-scale purposes because the span of bracketed ages is too great. Simple intrusives, in contrast with bracketed intrusives, provide only a minimum age pertaining to the rock that is intruded. Nevertheless, they are of some value.

Age determinations of glauconite in sedimentary rocks have been widely used to provide tie points. For age-dating purposes, it would be ideal if glauconite, which consists of a microcrystalline iron aluminum silicate, were always formed shortly after sedimentation. Unfortunately, there is no assurance that glauconite has formed this promptly; some glauconite aggregates may have continued to form long after deposition of the initial sediment. Furthermore, the likelihood of loss of both argon and strontium from glauconite adds to the uncertainty surrounding potassium-argon and rubidium-strontium age determinations based on glauconite.

Table 13 lists some of a much larger number of radiometric dates that have been considered in constructing a quantitative scale of time. The dates listed are of varying reliability both from a stratigraphic position and quantitative age points of view.

The quantitative scale of time has undergone continual modification as additional tie points have become available. Analytical techniques have continued to improve, along with increased understanding of the limitations of the various age-dating methods. Looking to the future, we can foresee a scale of geologic time in which there are an increasing number of tie points, and in which the calculated ages are of greater reliability.

REFERENCES

FAUL, HENRY, *Ages of Rocks, Planets and Stars*. New York: McGraw-Hill Book Co., 1966. (Readable authoritative account of modern age dating methods and of problems in establishing a quantitative scale of geologic time.)

HAMILTON, E. I., *Applied Geochronology*. London & New York: Academic Press, 1965. (A detailed description of age dating methods in use today.)

HURLEY, PATRICK M., *How Old Is the Earth?* Garden City: Anchor Books, Doubleday and Company, 1959. (A readable, authoritative introduction to radiometric dating.)

HOLMES, ARTHUR, *Principles of Physical Geology*. New York: Ronald Press Co., 1965. (A list of radiometric ages used in construction of a geologic time scale is provided in Chapter 13.)

KNOPF, ADOLPH, "Measuring Geologic Time," *Scientific Monthly*, 85: 225-236, 1957.

KULP, J. L., "Geologic Time Scale," *Science*, 133: 1105-1114, 1961. (Tabulates critical radiometric dates that apply to geologic time scale since start of Cambrian Period.)

RANKAMA, KALERVO, *Isotope Geology*. New York: Pergamon Press, 1965. (Chapter 5 provides a detailed account of physics and mathematics of radioactivity.)

RUSSELL, R. D. and FARQUHAR, R. M., *Lead Isotopes in Geology*. New York: Interscience Publisher, 1960. (Detailed treatment of use of lead isotope methods.)

WOODFORD, A. O., *Historical Geology*. San Francisco: W. H. Freeman and Co., 1965. (Chapter 8 provides good account of radiometric age dating.)

TABLE 13

Some radiometric dates that have been applied to geologic time scale. Adapted from various sources. Dates listed here are not necessarily those used by other persons who have compiled time scales.

Epoch or Period	Stratigraphic Position	Locality	Rock Type	Mineral Analyzed	Radiometric Dating Method	Age in Millions of Yrs.
Pleistocene	Pleistocene–Pliocene boundary	Sierra Nevada California	Tuff	Biotite	Potassium–argon	1.0 ± 0.5
Pliocene	Latest Pliocene	Sutter Buttes California	Rhyolite	Biotite	Potassium–argon	1.7 ± 0.4
	Pliocene–Miocene boundary	Nevada	Rhyolite Tuff	Biotite	Potassium–argon	12 ± 0.5
Miocene	Middle Miocene	Colorado	Granite	Monazite	Uranium–lead	16 ± 0.5
		Washington	Granite	Biotite	Potassium–argon	17 ± 0.5
	Lower Miocene	Austria	Sandstone	Glauconite	Potassium–argon	25 ± 1
Oligocene		Oregon	Tuff	Biotite	Potassium–argon	25.7 ± 0.8
		Texas	Tuff	Biotite	Potassium–argon	33.1 ± 1.0
Eocene	Upper Eocene	USSR	Granite	Biotite	Potassium–argon	38 ± 4
	Mid-lower Eocene	Texas	Sandstone	Glauconite	Potassium–argon	52 ± 2
	Lowermost Eocene	New Jersey	Sandstone	Glauconite	Potassium–argon	62 ± 2
Paleocene		Colorado	Ore	Pitchblende	Uranium–lead	59 ± 2
Cretaceous	Uppermost Cretaceous	Alberta	Coal Seam	Biotite	Potassium–argon	63 ± 2
	Mid-upper Cretaceous	Germany	Sandstone	Glauconite	Potassium–argon	81 ± 2
	Uppermost Lower Cretaceous	USSR	Sandstone	Glauconite	Potassium–argon	117 ± 12
Jurassic	Upper Jurassic	California	Granite	Biotite	Potassium–argon	127 ± 4
	Middle Jurassic	Georgia	Granite	Biotite	Potassium–argon	165 ± 3
Triassic	Upper Triassic	New Jersey	Diabase	Biotite	Potassium–argon	195 ± 4
	Middle Triassic	Arizona		Pitchblende	Uranium–lead	218 ± 5

Period	Subdivision	Location	Rock type	Mineral	Method	Age
Permian	Middle Permian	USSR	Evaporite sequence	Sylvite	Potassium-calcium	241 ± 8
	Lower Permian	Norway	Nordmarkite	Zircon	Uranium-lead	260 ± 5
Pennsylvanian	Upper Pennsylvanian	Australia	Toscanite	Biotite	Potassium-argon	287 ± 9
Mississippian	Lower Mississippian	USSR	Granite	Biotite	Potassium-argon	340 ± 10
Devonian	Upper Devonian	Australia	Lava	Biotite	Potassium-argon	350
	Lower Devonian	England	Granite	Biotite	Potassium-argon & rubidium-strontium	395 ± 5
Silurian	Lower Silurian	Ohio	Sandstone	Glauconite	Potassium-argon	410 ± 15
Ordovician	Upper Middle Ordovician	Alabama	Bentonite	Zircon	Uranium-lead	445 ± 10
		Sweden	Bentonite	Sandstone	Potassium-argon	452
				Biotite	Rubidium-strontium	447
Cambrian	Upper Cambrian	Sweden	Shale	Whole rock	Uranium-lead	500
	Middle Cambrian	USSR	Rhyolite	Glauconite	Potassium-argon	533 ± 50
	Lower Cambrian	USSR	Rhyolite	Glauconite	Potassium-argon	577 ± 58
	Lower Cambrian	USSR	Rhyolite		Potassium-argon	610 ± 61
Precambrian		Finland	samples from same deposit	Galena	Lead-207/lead-206	775
		Quebec		Thorianite	Uranium-lead	965 ± 20
		Quebec	samples from same deposit	Biotite	Potassium-argon	965 ± 55
				Phlogopite	Potassium-argon	1060 ± 65
		Australia		Uraninite	Uranium-lead	1070 ± 25
		Arizona		Monazite	Uranium-lead	1190
		Scotland	Granite	Biotite	Rubidium-strontium	1300
		Arizona	Gneiss	Biotite	Rubidium-strontium	1470 ± 55
		Finland	Pegmatite	Muscovite	Rubidium-strontium	1530
		Ukraine		Galena	Lead-207/lead-206	1800
		Ontario		Monazite	Uranium-lead	200 ± 100
		Quebec	Rhyolite	Biotite	Rubidium-strontium	2215
		Finland	Granodiorite	Galena	Potassium-argon	2400
		Ukraine		Galena	Lead-207/lead-206	2530
			Gneiss	Orthite	Uranium-lead	2700 ± 100

SUMMARY OUTLINE

Nature of atoms
Electrons, neutrons and protons
Atomic number and mass number
Nuclides and isotopes

Nature of radioactivity
Spontaneous disintegration
Types of particles produced in disintegration: alpha particles,
beta particles, neutrinos and gamma rays
Mass to energy transformation
Alternative decay routes

Probability and radioactivity
Uncertainty and individual atoms
Decay constant and half-life
Law of radioactive decay

Naturally occurring radioactive nuclides
Nuclides produced by neutron bombardment
Long-lived radioactive nuclides
Single-step decay versus series-decay
Uranium and thorium series

Decay clocks
Carbon-14 clock

Accumulation clocks
Uranium-lead and thorium-lead methods
Concordant and discordant ages
Potassium-argon methods
Rubidium-strontium methods

Establishing quantitative geologic time scale

Index